Kids Learn!

Getting Ready for

3rd Grade

Publishing Credits

Conni Medina, M.A.Ed., *Managing Editor*; Robin Erickson, *Production Director*; Lee Aucoin, *Creative Director*; Timothy J. Bradley, *Illustration Manager*; Aubrie Nielsen, M.S.Ed., *Senior Editor*; Caroline Gasca, M.S.Ed., *Editor*; Melina Sánchez, *Assistant Editor*; Marissa Rodriguez, *Designer*; Stephanie Reid, *Photo Editor*; Rachelle Cracchiolo, M.S.Ed., *Publisher*

Image Credits

All images Shutterstock.

Teacher Created Materials

5301 Oceanus Drive
Huntington Beach, CA 92649-1030
http://www.tcmpub.com
ISBN 978-1-4333-2535-9
© 2014 Teacher Created Materials, Inc.

Table of Contents

Índice de materias

Welcome to Kids Learn!

Dear Family,

Welcome to *Kids Learn! Getting Ready for 3rd Grade*. Third grade will be an exciting year. There will be plenty of new learning opportunities, including longer books to read and multiplication facts to memorize! Interesting new topics in science and social studies will keep students engaged in lessons at school.

Kids Learn! was designed to help solidify the concepts your child learned in second grade and help your child prepare for the year ahead. The activities are based on college and career readiness standards and provide practice with essential skills for the grade level. Keeping reading, writing, and math skills sharp while your child is on break from school will help his or her third grade year get off to a great start. There is also a section at the end of the book that provides practice for standardized testing.

Keep these tips in mind as you work with your child through the *Kids Learn!* book:

- Set aside a **specific time each day** to work on the activities.

- **Complete one language arts and one mathematics page** each time your child works in the book rather than an entire week's worth of activity pages at one time.

- Keep all **practice sessions with your child positive and constructive.** If the mood becomes tense or if either of you gets frustrated, set the book aside and find another time for your child to practice.

- **Help your child with instructions,** if necessary. If your child is having difficulty understanding what to do, work some of the problems through together.

- Encourage your child to do his or her best work and **compliment the effort that goes into learning.** Celebrate the completion of all the activities by filling in the certificate at the end of the book and displaying it in a special place.

Enjoy the time learning with your child during his or her vacation from school. Third grade will be here before you know it!

Bienvenidos a Kids Learn!

Querida familia:

Bienvenidos a *Kids Learn! Getting Ready for 3rd Grade*. El tercer grado será un año emocionante. ¡Habrá bastantes nuevas oportunidades para aprender, incluyendo libros más largos para leer y operaciones de multiplicación para memorizar! Nuevos temas interesantes en las ciencias y los estudios sociales mantendrán a los estudiantes involucrados en las lecciones escolares.

Kids Learn! fue diseñado para ayudar a consolidar los conceptos que su hijo aprendió en el segundo grado y para ayudar a su hijo a prepararse para el año que viene. Las actividades están basadas en las Normas de preparación para la universidad y el trabajo y proveen práctica con las destrezas esenciales para el nivel de ese grado. Mantener a punto las destrezas de la lectura, la escritura y las matemáticas mientras su hijo está de descanso de la escuela ayudará a que el año del tercer grado comience de gran manera. También hay una sección al final del libro que provee práctica para los exámenes estandarizados.

Tenga en cuenta estos consejos mientras completa junto con su hijo el libro de *Kids Learn!*:

- Reserve un **tiempo específico todos los días** para trabajar en las actividades.
- **Complete una página de artes del lenguaje y una página de matemáticas** cada vez que su hijo trabaja con el libro, en lugar de completar al mismo tiempo las páginas de actividades que se completarían en una semana.
- Mantenga todas las **sesiones de práctica con su hijo positivas y constructivas.** Si el estado de ánimo se pone tenso, o usted y su hijo se frustran, ponga el libro a un lado y busque otro momento para la práctica.
- **Ayude a su hijo con las instrucciones**, si es necesario. Si a su hijo se le dificulta entender qué hacer, hagan algunos de los problemas juntos.
- Anime a su hijo a que haga su mejor esfuerzo y **elogie el empeño que se dedica cuando se aprende.** Celebre la terminación de todas las actividades llenando el certificado que se encuentra al final del libro y poniéndolo en un lugar especial.

Disfrute el tiempo en el que aprende con su hijo durante sus vacaciones de la escuela. ¡El tercer grado llegará antes de que se dé cuenta!

Top 10 Things Your Third Grader Will Need to Know

1. **Word identification strategies** when reading new words (e.g., root words, chunks, prefixes, suffixes)

2. **Ways language is used in writing** (e.g., similes, metaphors, personification, imagery)

3. **Research skills** such as using encyclopedias, nonfiction books, and the Internet for a research project

4. **Multiplication and division** within 100

5. **Fractions**

6. Area and perimeter of **one-dimensional shapes**

7. The **water cycle**

8. **Earth** is one of several planets that orbit the sun, and the moon orbits Earth

9. **Ideas about government**, civic life, and politics

10. **Selective societies** in Africa, the Americas, Asia, and Europe

Las 10 cosas que su hijo de tercer grado debe saber

1. **Estrategias de identificación de palabras** al leer palabras nuevas (p. ej. raíces de palabras, terminaciones, prefijos, sufijos)

2. **Modos en que se utiliza la lengua escrita** (p. ej. símiles, metáforas, personificación, imaginería)

3. **Aptitudes de investigación,** como por ejemplo usar enciclopedias, libros de no ficción e Internet para un proyecto de investigación

4. **Multiplicación y división** hasta 100

5. **Fracciones**

6. Área y perímetro de **formas unidimensionales**

7. El **ciclo del agua**

8. **La Tierra** es uno de varios planetas que giran alrededor del sol y la luna gira alrededor de la Tierra

9. **Ideas sobre el gobierno**, la vida civil y la política

10. Ciertas **sociedades** de África, América, Asia y Europa

© *Teacher Created Materials*

#13535—Kids Learn! Getting Ready for 3rd Grade

7

Things to Do at Home

To Develop Healthy Habits

SCHEDULE

4:00	Snack
4:30	Piano practice
5:00	Set the table, feed the dog
5:30	**Dinner**
6:30	Homework and reading time
7:15	Free time (after homework)
7:45	Get ready for bed

- Make sure your child gets plenty of sleep. Children this age need 10–11 hours of sleep each night. Take time to establish bedtime routines that involve relaxing activities, such as taking a warm shower or reading.

- Help your child become organized and responsible. Have places for your child to keep important things. Take time to set up a schedule together. Use a timer to keep track of time spent on different activities.

- Have conversations with your child. Ask your child questions about his or her activities and tell your child stories about funny things that happened to you.

To Practice Reading

- Set a reading time for the entire family. Make sure your child chooses books that are at a comfortable reading level, and that are interesting to him or her. See the Suggested Vacation Reading list on page 16.

- Create a family award for the best book of the month. Take turns reading an assortment of books and vote on which ones have the best writing or illustrations.

- Write notes or letters to your child, asking questions to which he or she must respond.

To Practice Writing

- Encourage your child to write letters or emails to friends and family members who live out of town.

- Dictate your grocery list or your child's weekly chores and have your child record the list.

- Have your child keep a diary or journal about activities he or she is doing during time off from school.

To Practice Math

- Let your child keep score as the family plays games so that he or she has to calculate the points that each participant has earned.

- Turn everyday tasks into math problems. For example: *There are 4 people in our family. We need 4 spoons for soup and 4 spoons for ice cream. How many spoons do we need in total?*

- Involve your child in cooking the family dinner. You can have your child help you by measuring the ingredients. This is a great way to teach about liquid and dry units of measure.

Cosas para hacer en casa

Para desarrollar hábitos saludables

- Asegúrese de que su hijo duerma lo suficiente. Los niños de esta edad necesitan dormir de 10 a 11 horas todas las noches. Tome tiempo para establecer rutinas para la hora de dormir que incluyan actividades relajantes, como bañarse con agua tibia o leer.

- Ayude a que su hijo sea organizado y responsable. Tenga lugares para que su hijo guarde cosas importantes. Tome tiempo para que juntos hagan un horario. Use un temporizador para estar al tanto del tiempo que dura cada actividad.

- Tenga conversaciones con su hijo. Haga preguntas a su hijo sobre sus actividades y cuéntele historias sobre cosas graciosas que le han ocurrido a usted.

HORARIO

4:00	Refrigerio
4:30	Práctica de piano
5:00	Poner la mesa, darle de comer al perro
5:30	Cena
6:30	Tarea y hora de leer
7:15	Tiempo libre (después de la tarea)
7:45	Prepararme para dormir

Para practicar la lectura

- Establezca una hora de lectura para toda la familia. Asegúrese de que su hijo escoja libros que estén a un nivel de lectura adecuado y que le sean interesantes. Vea la lista de *Lectura sugerida para las vacaciones* en la página 16.

- Cree un premio familiar para el mejor libro del mes. Tomen turnos para leer una diversidad de libros y voten sobre cuáles están mejor escritos o tienen mejores ilustraciones.

- Escriba notas o cartas para su hijo con preguntas a las cuales debe responder.

10

#13535—Kids Learn! Getting Ready for 3rd Grade

© Teacher Created Materials

Para practicar la escritura

- Anime a su hijo a que escriba cartas o correos electrónicos a amigos y familiares que viven fuera de la ciudad.

- Dicte la lista del mandado o los quehaceres semanales de su hijo y pídale que anote la lista.

- Pida a su hijo que lleve un diario o una agenda sobre las actividades que hace durante su tiempo de descanso de la escuela.

Para practicar las matemáticas

- Deje que su hijo lleve la cuenta de los puntos durante los juegos de la familia para que tenga que calcular los puntos que ha ganado cada participante.

- Convierta tareas cotidianas en problemas matemáticos. Por ejemplo: *Hay 4 personas en nuestra familia. Necesitamos 4 cucharas para la sopa y 4 cucharas para el helado. ¿Cuántas cucharas necesitamos en total?*

- Involucre a su hijo cuando prepare la cena familiar. Puede pedir a su hijo que ayude a medir los ingredientes. Esta es una gran manera para enseñar las unidades de medidas líquidas y secas.

Things to Do in the Community

To Develop Good Citizenship

- Volunteer with your child in a community organization.

- Encourage your child to organize a fund-raising event, such as a lemonade stand or garage sale, to raise money for a charitable cause. Help your child carry out the event and deliver the money earned to the organization.

- Discuss with your child the character traits of good citizens, such as following rules, helping others, playing fairly, and helping to keep a place clean. Encourage your child to point out people in the community who they notice exhibiting good citizenship.

To Practice Reading

- Take regular trips to the library, encouraging your child to select a wide range of reading materials in both fiction and nonfiction.

- Help your child read street signs, bus schedules, store signs, park rules, and restaurant menus when you are out in the community.

- When visiting attractions such as museums, encourage your child to read the signs or museum guides describing the exhibits.

Things to Do in the Community (cont.)

To Practice Writing

- After visiting interesting locations such as parks, museums, or stores, help your child write about what he or she saw and what he or she felt about the visits. Keep these writings in a notebook as memories of these adventures.

- Provide your child with a small notebook before leaving on a community outing so that he or she can take notes and draw pictures about the activity.

- Discuss with your child the role that community helpers such as police officers, firefighters, trash collectors, and health workers play. Have your child write thank-you notes to any of these workers. Take your child to the post office to mail the letters, or personally deliver them.

To Practice Math

- Have your child identify coins needed for a purchase. For example: *This can of corn costs 79 cents. Which coins would I need to buy this can?*

- Have your child estimate measurements while out in the community. For example: *This menu is about 8 inches wide. About how wide do you think the table is?*

- Have your child identify and describe geometric shapes such as rectangles, squares, circles, and triangles. Encourage your child to define the shape by its attributes, such as number of sides, vertices (corners), and angles. For example: *Can you find a sign that is a rectangle? How many sides does it have?*

Cosas para hacer en la comunidad

Para ser un buen ciudadano

- Haga trabajo voluntario junto con su hijo en una organización comunitaria.

- Anime a su hijo a que organice un evento de recaudación de fondos, como un puesto de limonada o una venta de garaje para obtener fondos para una buena causa. Ayude a su hijo a llevar a cabo el evento y a entregar el dinero a la organización.

- Hable con su hijo sobre los rasgos de personalidad de los buenos ciudadanos, como seguir las reglas, ayudar a los demás, jugar limpio y ayudar a mantener limpio un lugar. Anime a su hijo a que indique gente en la comunidad de quien se da cuenta que demuestran ser buenos ciudadanos.

Para practicar la lectura

- Visiten la biblioteca a menudo y anime a su hijo a que escoja una amplia gama de material de lectura, tanto de ficción como de no ficción.

- Ayude a su hijo a leer letreros de las calles, horarios de autobuses, reglas de los parques y menús de restaurantes cuando anden por la comunidad.

- Cuando visiten atracciones tales como museos, anime a su hijo a que lea los letreros o guías de museos que describen las exhibiciones.

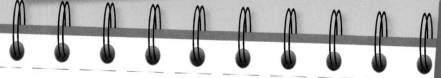

Para practicar la escritura

- Después de visitar lugares interesantes como parques, museos o tiendas, ayude a su hijo a que escriba sobre qué vio y cómo se sintió sobre estas visitas. Guarde estos apuntes en un cuaderno como recuerdos de estas aventuras.

- Provea a su hijo de un pequeño cuaderno antes de salir de excursión a la comunidad para que pueda tomar apuntes y hacer dibujos sobre tal actividad.

- Hable con su hijo sobre el rol que juegan los ayudantes de la comunidad como oficiales de policía, bomberos, basureros y trabajadores de la salud. Pida a su hijo que escriba notas de agradecimiento a cualquiera de estos trabajadores. Lleve a su hijo a la oficina de correos para enviar las cartas, o entréguenlas personalmente.

Para practicar las matemáticas

- Pida a su hijo que identifique las monedas necesarias para una compra. Por ejemplo: *Esta lata de maíz cuesta 79 centavos. ¿Qué monedas necesitaría para comprar esta lata?*

- Pida a su hijo que calcule medidas mientras andan por la comunidad. Por ejemplo: *Este menú tiene como 8 pulgadas de ancho. ¿Qué tan ancha crees que es la mesa?*

- Pida a su hijo que identifique y describa figuras geométricas, como rectángulos, cuadrados, círculos y triángulos. Anímelo a que defina una imagen por medio de sus características, como el número de lados, vértices (esquinas) y ángulos. Por ejemplo: *¿Puedes encontrar un letrero que es un rectángulo? ¿Cuántos lados tiene?*

Suggested Vacation Reading
Lectura sugerida para las vacaciones

These books are recommended for students in second and third grades. Most, if not all, of these books are available at your local library or bookstore. Encourage your child to read daily and record his or her reading progress on the Vacation Reading Log on page 17.

Estos libros son recomendados para estudiantes de segundo y tercer grado. La mayoría, si no todos estos libros, están disponibles en su biblioteca o librería local. Anime a su hijo a que lea diariamente y registre el progreso de su lectura en el Registro de lectura de las vacaciones en la página 17.

Fiction

The Fire Cat by Esther Averill
Superfudge by Judy Blume
Beezus and Ramona by Beverly Cleary
How the Camel Got His Hump by Rudyard Kipling
Magic Tree House series by Mary Pope Osborne
Captain Underpants series by Dav Pilkey
Cowgirl Kate and Cocoa by Erica Silverman
Amos & Boris by William Steig
Charlotte's Web by E. B. White
Nim's Island by Wendy Orr

Nonfiction

Step into the Rainforest by Howard Rice
Volcano: The Eruption and Healing of Mount St. Helens by Patricia Lauber
26 Fairmount Avenue by Tomie dePaola
Sixteen Years in Sixteen Seconds: The Sammy Lee Story by Paula Yoo
My Senator and Me: A Dog's Eye View of Washington, D.C. by Edward M. Kennedy
My Librarian Is a Camel: How Books Are Brought to Children Around the World by Margriet Ruurs
Living Color by Steve Jenkins
Bill Peet: An Autobiography by Bill Peet
Amos Fortune, Free Man by Elizabeth Yates
The Great Fire by Jim Murphy

Vacation Reading Log
Registro de lectura de las vacaciones

Help your child complete this reading log to keep track of his or her vacation reading.

Ayude a su hijo a completar este registro de lectura para llevar la cuenta de su lectura durante las vacaciones.

Date *Fecha*	Title *Título*	Number of pages *Número de páginas*

Websites and Apps for Parents and Kids
Páginas web y aplicaciones para padres y niños

Language Arts Websites

Reading Rockets
http://www.readingrockets.org
Information, activities, and advice for parents

Book Adventure
http://www.bookadventure.com
Book quizzes for many different books

Read Write Think
http://www.readwritethink.org
/parent-afterschool-resources/
Student materials that support literacy learning in the K–12 classroom

International Children's Digital Library
http://en.childrenslibrary.org
Online database of e-books organized by age, reading level, language, genre, or interest

K12 Reader
http://www.k12reader.com
Instruction tips, worksheets, and activities for helping students learn to read

Mathematics Websites

PBS Early Math
http://www.pbs.org/parents/education
/math/milestones/first-second-grade
Math-based activities and developmental milestones for children from 6 to 9 years old

Figure This! Math Challenges for Families
http://www.figurethis.org
Math problems to challenge families

Funbrain
http://www.funbrain.com/brain
/MathBrain/MathBrain.html
Fun, arcade-style games covering a variety of math concepts

SoftSchools.com
http://www.softschools.com/math
/Math concepts, tips, games, and activity sheets

Education.com
http://www.education.com/activity/math/
Suggestions for math games to make and play at home

En español

Mundo Latino
http://www.mundolatino.org
Base de datos extensiva para hispanohablantes con enlaces a diferentes temas, juegos educativos y revistas en la red

StoryPlace
http://www.storyplace.org/sp/storyplace.
asp
Una biblioteca digital con páginas llenas de cuentos para niños, jóvenes y adultos

¡Colorín Colorado!
http://www.colorincolorado.org
Información, actividades y consejos para padres y maestros de estudiantes que hablan español

Aplicaciones Didácticas
http://www.aplicaciones.info/lectura/
lectura.htm#peques
Base de datos de cuentos cortos y preguntas de comprensión correspondientes

Cibercuentos
http://www.cibercuentos.org
Una serie de cuentos interactivos en español para las edades 3–8 años

Fun Educational Apps

Explor-eBook
Teacher Created Materials, Inc.
A library of hundreds of interactive eBook titles offer engaging reading practice across grade levels and content areas

Brain Quest® Blast Off
Modality, Inc.
Nearly 2,000 trivia questions from categories such as Language Arts, Math, Science, and Social Studies

Math BINGO
ABCya.com
Choose from five different BINGO games at three levels of difficulty

KickBox
MIND Research Institute
Visual problem solving at seven progressive levels

Weekly Activities for Students

Actividades semanales para estudiantes

Digraphs

Directions: Add one of the four digraphs—*ch, sh, th, wh*—to each letter group. Say the words you have formed.

Instrucciones: *Agrega uno de los cuatro dígrafos—ch, sh, th, wh—a cada grupo de letras. Pronuncia las palabras que formaste.*

Tip

When two consonants are placed together to form one consonant sound, it is called a *digraph*. *Ch, sh, th*, and *wh* are the most common digraphs. Digraphs can come at the beginning, middle, or end of a word.

Cuando dos consonantes están puestas juntas y forman un solo sonido de consonante, se llaman un dígrafo. *Ch, sh, th, y* wh *son los dígrafos más comunes. Los dígrafos pueden ocurrir al principio, en el medio o al final de una palabra.*

1. __th__ick

2. _____oose

3. _____ape

4. ma_____

5. _____ank

6. _____eck

7. _____irst

8. _____istle

9. wi_____

10. _____ip

11. ben_____

12. tra_____

Comparing Numbers

Directions: Write the correct *less than* or *greater than* symbol between each pair of numbers.

Instrucciones: *Escribe el símbolo correcto de* más que *o* menos que *entre cada par de números.*

Tip

< is the symbol for *less than*
< *es el símbolo para* menos que

> is the symbol for *greater than*
> *es el símbolo para* más que

50 **>** 37

1. 201 (**>**) 101

2. 372 ( ) 273

3. 350 ( ) 140

4. 641 ( ) 515

5. 199 ( ) 910

6. 795 ( ) 974

7. 132 ( ) 601

8. 976 ( ) 147

9. 300 ( ) 315

10. 250 ( ) 170

11. 430 ( ) 340

12. 807 ( ) 750

13. 150 ( ) 100

14. 629 ( ) 702

15. 321 ( ) 394

Double Trouble

Directions: Write the word that names each picture. Use a hyphen to divide it into syllables.

Instrucciones: *Escribe la palabra que nombra cada imagen. Usa un guión para separarla en sílabas.*

Tip

When two consonants come between two vowels in a word, the word is usually divided between the two consonants.

Cuando dos consonantes están entre dos vocales en una palabra, la palabra usualmente se divide entre las dos consonantes.

Examples: bat-ter   mar-ket   car-pet

1.

ham-mer

2.

3.

4.

5.

6.

7.

8.

9.

#13535—Kids Learn! Getting Ready for 3rd Grade

Addition Practice

Directions: Solve each problem.

Instrucciones: *Resuelve cada problema.*

1.
```
    528
+   261
```

2.
```
    117
+   760
```

3.
```
    425
+   362
```

4.
```
    872
+   114
```

5.
```
    341
+   528
```

6.
```
    192
+   604
```

7.
```
    431
+   135
```

8.
```
    588
+   311
```

9.
```
    376
+   401
```

10.
```
    349
+   640
```

11.
```
    174
+   721
```

12.
```
    575
+   203
```

13.
```
    513
+   123
```

14.
```
    229
+   110
```

15.
```
    306
+   481
```

16.
```
    609
+   280
```

Capital Review

Directions: Circle all the letters below that should be capitals. *Hint:* There are 53 of them.

Instrucciones: *Encierra con un círculo todas las letras de abajo que deben ser mayúsculas.* Pista: *Hay 53 de ellas.*

1. (t)he first day of school is exciting.

2. freddy wilson's frog, peepers, hopped into mrs. woolsey's purse.

3. the fourth thursday in november is thanksgiving.

4. i like halloween best when it is on a saturday.

5. aunt susan went to yellowstone national park.

6. connie lives on maple street in bismarck, north dakota.

7. brazil, argentina, and peru are in south america.

8. the mediterranean sea and the atlantic ocean touch spain.

9. the letter was signed, "love always, esther."

10. davis medical center opened in january last year.

11. we visited my friend youko in japan.

12. last tuesday, ruben walked his dog, spotty, down tulip street to central park.

Measuring Length

Directions: Use a ruler to measure each inchworm. Write on the line how many inches each worm is.

Instrucciones: *Usa una regla para medir cada gusano. Escribe en la línea cuántas pulgadas mide cada gusano.*

1. _____**3**_____ inches

2. _____ inches

3. _____ inches

4. _____ inches

5. _____ inches

6. _____ inches

7. _____ inches

8. _____ inches

Sentence Scramble

Directions: Unscramble the words to make sentences. Start each sentence with a capital letter and end with a punctuation mark.

Instrucciones: *Ordena las palabras para formar oraciones. Asegúrate de empezar cada oración con mayúscula y con la puntuación correcta.*

1. bird cat the chased the

  The cat chased the bird.

  _____

2. letter friend I a wrote my to

  _____

  _____

3. trip the took a family

  _____

  _____

4. a baker cake baked the

  _____

  _____

5. sea jumped into penguin a the

  _____

  _____

6. song to a puppets audience the sang the

  _____

  _____

Money Problems

Directions: Solve each money problem.

Instrucciones: *Resuelve cada problema de dinero.*

1. Donna spent 5¢ more than Susie. Susie spent 28¢. How much did Donna spend?

_____

2. Derek has 50¢. He buys a comic book and now has 20¢ left. How much was the comic book?

_____

3. José and Lin both went shopping and received some change back. José received twice as much change as Lin, who got 12¢ back in change. How much change did José get back?

_____

4. Nihal had a $5 bill. He went shopping and received $1.50 in change. How much did he spend?

_____

5. Write your own money number story. Find the answer, and write a number sentence to go with it.

_____

_____

_____

Story Detective

Directions: Choose a fiction book to read. Answer the questions below about the book.

Instrucciones: *Lee un libro de ficción. En cada uno de los espacios responde a la pregunta sobre el libro.*

Book Title

_____

Who are the main characters?

_____

What happened?

_____

When did it happen?

_____

Where did it happen?

_____

Why did it happen?

_____

How did it happen?

_____

Hundreds, Tens, and Ones

Directions: Write the number shown with the base-ten blocks.

Instrucciones: *Escribe el número que se muestra con los bloques del sistema decimal.*

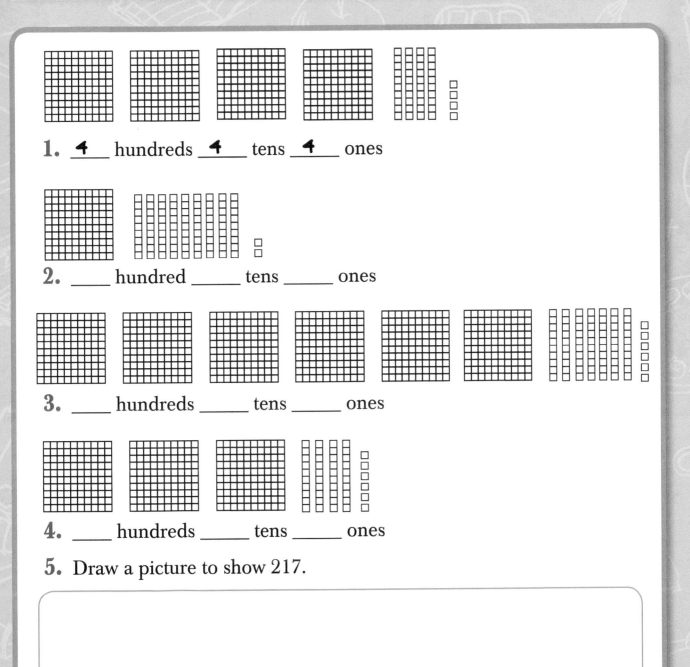

1. __4__ hundreds __4__ tens __4__ ones

2. ____ hundred ____ tens ____ ones

3. ____ hundreds ____ tens ____ ones

4. ____ hundreds ____ tens ____ ones

5. Draw a picture to show 217.

What Do You Think?

Directions: Choose a book, a television show, or a game. Tell your opinion about it. Give reasons why you like it or do not like it. Use words like *because*, *and*, and *also* to connect your ideas. End with a closing sentence.

Instrucciones: *Escoje un libro, una serie de televisión o un juego. Di tu opinión al respecto. Da razones por qué te gusta o no te gusta. Usa palabras como* because, and *y* also *para conectar tus ideas. Termina con una oración de conclusión.*

Lemonade for Sale

Directions: Read the passage, then answer the questions.

Instrucciones: *Lee el pasaje, luego contesta las preguntas.*

Ann and Lucy wanted to go to the movies. But they did not have money. They tried washing dogs. It was too messy. They tried babysitting. It took too much time. They decided to have a lemonade stand.

The next day was hot and dry. It was a good day for a lemonade stand. The girls mixed the cold drinks. They poured the drinks into a plastic pitcher. They sold the drinks for 50 cents each.

Ten kids and two adults bought the drinks. Ann and Lucy each needed three dollars for the movies. They made enough money. Hooray! They were on their way.

1. What is one trait that the main characters of this story share?

_____

_____

2. How does the author show that trait in the characters?

_____

_____

3. What is another way the characters could have solved the problem?

_____

_____

What Is 100 More?

Directions: Use mental math to solve each problem.

Instrucciones: Usa matemáticas mentales para resolver cada problema.

1. $140 + 100 =$ **240**

2. $815 + 100 =$ _____

3. $620 + 100 =$ _____

4. $150 + 100 =$ _____

5. $650 + 100 =$ _____

6. $265 + 100 =$ _____

7. $100 + 265 =$ _____

8. $100 + 560 =$ _____

9. $100 + 765 =$ _____

10. $100 + 870 =$ _____

11. $100 + 275 =$ _____

12. $100 + 280 =$ _____

13. Explain your strategy for adding 100 to a number.

_____

_____

_____

_____

Contraction Action

Directions: Write the correct contraction in the blank.

Instrucciones: *Escribe la contracción correcta en el espacio en blanco.*

Tip

A *contraction* is a word that combines two words. An apostrophe takes the place of one or more letters.

Una contracción *es una palabra que combina dos palabras. Un apóstrofo toma el lugar de una o más letras.*

1. _____**What's**_____ your friend's name? (What is)

2. I think _____ be sunny tomorrow. (it will)

3. Our friends said _____ come with us to the beach. (they would)

4. Do you know if _____ food at the beach? (there is)

5. _____ going to drive us there? (Who is)

6. We _____ taken the bus to the beach. (could have)

Number Names

Directions: Follow the directions below to name each number.

Instrucciones: Sigue las instrucciones de abajo para nombrar cada número.

Write each number using base-ten numerals.

Escribe cada número usando numerales del sistema decimal.

Example: one hundred sixty-nine: 169

1. seven hundred seventy-eight _____

2. four hundred six _____

3. two hundred thirty-three _____

4. four hundred ninety-one _____

Write each number in expanded notation.

Escribe cada número en notación desarrollada.

Example: $868 = 800 + 60 + 8$

5. $765 = $ _____ + _____ + _____

6. $557 = $ _____ + _____ + _____

Write the number name for each numeral.

Escribe el nombre del número para cada numeral.

Example: 418: four hundred eighteen

7. 129 _____

8. 365 _____

#13535—Kids Learn! Getting Ready for 3rd Grade

Keeping Cool!

Directions: Read the article. Then, answer the questions.

Instrucciones: *Lee el artículo. Luego, contesta las preguntas.*

Sweat It Out!

Have you ever wondered why you sweat on a hot day? Our bodies are mostly made of water. When we get hot, our bodies are hot inside. Our skin has sweat glands deep inside it. The glands pull the "hot" water from inside the body through the skin. There is a bit of sodium and other things in this fluid. When the sweat gets to the outside of the skin it feels moist. Then the sweat evaporates in the air. That feels cool and helps cool the body. But do not forget to drink lots of water on a hot day!

1. The word *sweat* means

    (A) the blood inside the body

    (B) the fluid from inside the body

    (C) the glands inside the body

2. The word *evaporate* means

    (A) to mix fluid in the body

    (B) to heat the water on the skin

    (C) to take fluid out in the air

Ones, Tens, and Hundreds

Directions: Write the numeral that represents the picture.

Instrucciones: Escribe el numeral que representa la imagen.

This bundle shows one hundred sticks.

This bundle shows ten sticks.

This shows two sticks.

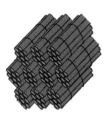

The number for the hundreds goes here.

The number for the tens goes here.

The number for the ones goes here.

112

1. What number is shown?

_____132_____

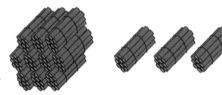

2. What number is shown?

_____

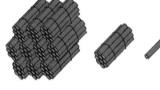

3. What number is shown?

_____

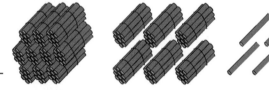

4. What number is shown?

_____

#13535—Kids Learn! Getting Ready for 3rd Grade

Revise It!

Directions: Revise the paragraph below to improve organization, sentence structure, and word choice. Rewrite the paragraph on a separate sheet of paper.

Instrucciones: Corrige el siguiente párrafo para mejorar la organización, la estructura de las oraciones y la selección de vocabulario. Reescribe el párrafo en una hoja de papel aparte.

- **Organization:** Put the sentences in the correct order—a topic sentence, supporting sentences, and a concluding sentence.

- **Sentence Structure:** Vary the order of the words in the sentences so that the sentences all have different beginnings.

- **Word Choice:** Add descriptive and specific words to make the topic more interesting. If possible, use a thesaurus to improve word variety.

- **Organización:** *Pon las oraciones en el orden correcto: una oración principal, oraciones de apoyo y una oración conclusiva.*

- **Estructura de las oraciones:** *Varía el orden de las palabras en las oraciones para que todas las oraciones comiencen diferente.*

- **Selección de vocabulario:** *Incluye palabras específicas y descriptivas para hacer más interesante el tema. Si es posible, usa un tesauro para aumentar la variedad de palabras.*

My Baby Brother

He made another mess by pulling out all the things I had hidden under the bed. He always makes a mess when he gets into my room. My baby brother is a pest. I want him locked out of my room forever. He got into my room yesterday while I was at school. He first took all of the pages out of one of my books. He also got into my closet and pulled all my clothes off the hangers. He should never be allowed to go into my room.

Skip Count By 100

Directions: Count by 100. Write the missing numbers.

Instrucciones: Cuenta de 100 en 100. Escribe los números que faltan.

1. 110, 210, __**310**__, 410, __**510**__, 610

2. 330, _____, 530, _____, _____, _____

3. _____, 240, _____, _____, _____, 640

4. 470, _____, _____, _____, 870, _____

5. 280, 380, _____, _____, _____, _____

6. 90, _____, _____, _____, _____, 590

7. 315, _____, _____, _____, 715, _____

8. 99, _____, 299, _____, _____, _____

9. 1, _____, 201, _____, _____, _____

10. 33, 133, _____, _____, _____, _____

#13535—Kids Learn! Getting Ready for 3rd Grade

Changing Irregular Verbs

Directions: Change the tense of the irregular verbs.

Instrucciones: Cambia el tiempo de los verbos irregulares.

Change the verbs below to past tense.

Cambia los verbos de abajo al tiempo pasado.

1. blow _____ **blew** _____

2. sing _____

3. wear _____

4. cry _____

5. make _____

6. fall _____

Change the verbs below to present tense.

Cambia los verbos de abajo al tiempo presente.

7. caught _____ **catch** _____

8. rode _____

9. paid _____

10. swept _____

11. read _____

12. took _____

Subtract Numbers

Directions: Solve the problems.

Instrucciones: *Resuelve los problemas.*

Problem Solving Steps

1. Show 43:
Muestra 43: ⑩ ⑩ ⑩ ⑩ ① ① ①

2. Regroup one 10 as ones.
Reagrupa un 10 como unidades. ⑩ ⑩ ⑩ ⑩̸ ① ① ①
① ① ① ① ①
① ① ① ① ①

3. Subtract 8 ones.
Resta 8 unidades. ⑩ ⑩ ⑩ ⑩̸ ⑩̸ ⑩̸
⑩̸ ⑩̸ ⑩̸ ⑩̸ ⑩̸
① ① ① ① ①

4. Subtract 2 tens.
Resta 2 unidades.

43 – 28 = 15 ⑩ ⑩̸ ⑩̸ ① ① ① ① ①

1.	2.	3.	4.
35	84	72	48
– 18	– 27	– 55	– 29

#13535—Kids Learn! Getting Ready for 3rd Grade

Happily Ever After?

Directions: Choose a fiction book to read. Think of a new ending for the story. Write it on the lines below.

Instrucciones: *Escoje un libro de ficción que quieras leer. Piensa en un nuevo final para la historia. Escríbelo en las líneas de abajo.*

Solar System

Directions: Read the text. Then, answer the questions.

Instrucciones: Lee el texto. Luego, contesta las preguntas.

A solar system has many parts. The sun is at the center. Around the sun are planets or other bodies. They all revolve around the sun. Think about our solar system. What do you know about it? It has a sun. It has eight planets. But that is not all. There are moons. There are comets and asteroids, too.

Here are some facts about our solar system:

- Neptune is a planet. It is the farthest from the sun.

- Jupiter is the biggest planet.

- Mercury is a planet. It is the closest to the sun.

- Saturn is known for its rings.

- Mars is known as the "red planet."

1. Which are not a part of our solar system?

(A) moons

(B) comets

(C) rockets

(D) planets

2. Which is the largest planet in our solar system?

_____

What's the Shape?

Directions: Use the Word Bank to label each shape. A word may be used more than once.

Instrucciones: *Usa el Banco de palabras para nombrar cada figura. Una palabra se puede usar más de una vez.*

Word Bank

triangle	quadrilateral	pentagon
hexagon	cube	

1.

_____

4.

_____

2.

_____

5.

_____

3.

_____

6.

_____

7. Draw a shape with five sides.

8. Draw a shape with three angles.

Irregular Plural Nouns

Directions: In the blanks, write the plural form of each underlined word.

Instrucciones: En los espacios en blanco, escribe el plural de cada palabra subrayada.

1. The <u>woman</u> next door invited several ____**women**____ to tea.

2. Although one baby <u>tooth</u> fell out, many more must fall out before I have all my adult _____.

3. One <u>man</u> on my father's bowling team is much taller than the other _____.

4. I saw only one <u>child</u>, but I could hear many more _____ playing.

5. It is much more difficult to hop on one <u>foot</u> than it is to hop on both _____.

6. We caught one <u>mouse</u> in the trap, but we suspected there were other _____ in the attic as well.

7. Su has one <u>fish</u> in her aquarium, but Lena has many _____.

8. One <u>wife</u> suggested that all of the _____ should meet for a morning walk.

9. The large <u>goose</u> bullied all the other _____ in the barnyard.

10. I added the hot <u>loaf</u> of bread to the other _____ I had baked in the morning.

Grouping for Multiplication

Directions: Circle the objects in each box to show equal groups. Then, complete the multiplication equation.

Instrucciones: Encierra con un círculo los objetos en cada cuadro para mostrar grupos iguales. Luego, completa la ecuación de multiplicación.

Example: 4 groups of 4

$4 \times 4 = 16$

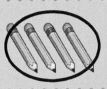

1. 6 groups of 2

$6 \times 2 = \boxed{}$

3. 5 groups of 4

$5 \times 4 = \boxed{}$

2. 3 groups of 6

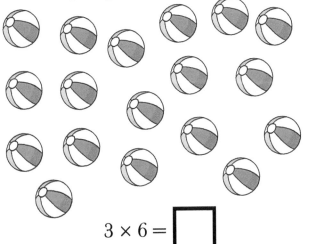

$3 \times 6 = \boxed{}$

4. 2 groups of 7

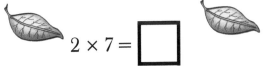

$2 \times 7 = \boxed{}$

Cause and Effect

Directions: Complete the activities below.

Instrucciones: Completa las actividades de abajo.

 **Tip**

A cause is the reason why something happens. The effect is what happens.
Una causa es la razón por lo cual algo pasa. El efecto es lo que pasa.

cause *(causa)*   **effect** *(efecto)*

Read each cause. Write an effect.
Lee cada causa. Escribe un efecto.

1. The class had perfect attendance.

    Each student in the class got an award.

2. The monkey ate all the bananas.

_____

3. The girl forgot her homework.

_____

Read each effect. Write a cause.
Lee cada efecto. Escribe una causa.

4. There was a traffic jam on the highway.

_____

5. Ice cream spilled on the floor.

_____

6. The baby started to cry.

_____

Picture Fractions

Directions: Write the fraction that shows which portion of each picture is shaded. Then, write the name of the fraction in words.

Instrucciones: *Escribe la fracción que muestra cuál porción de la imagen está sombreada. Luego, escribe el nombre de la fracción con palabras.*

Tip

A *fraction* names part of a whole or a group. The top number is the *numerator*. It tells how many parts of the whole you are describing. The bottom number is the *denominator*. It tells how many equal parts there are in all.

Una fracción *representa parte de un entero o de un grupo. El número de arriba es el* numerador. *Dice cuántas partes del entero estás describiendo. El número de abajo es el* denominador. *Dice cuántas partes iguales hay en total.*

$\dfrac{1}{2}$ ← **numerator** (shaded part)
← **denominator** (number of equal parts)

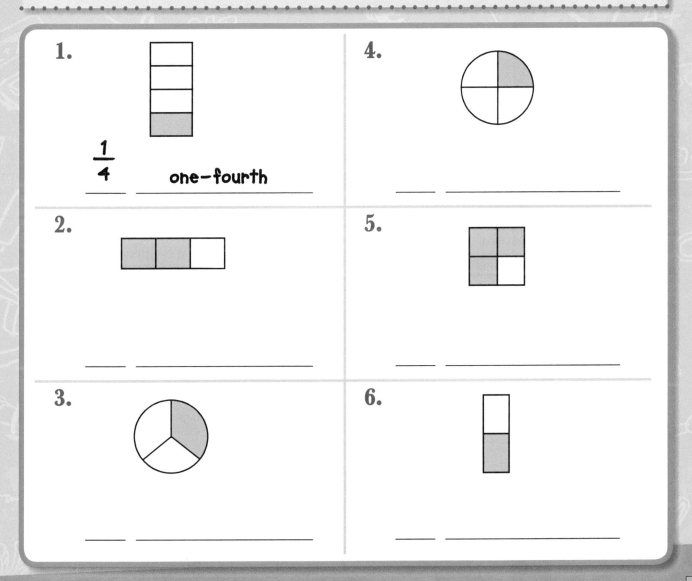

1.

$\dfrac{1}{4}$ one-fourth

2.

3.

4.

5.

6.

Start with a Noun and a Verb

Directions: Match each noun to a verb. Then, write a sentence for each noun/verb pair.

Instrucciones: Une cada sustantivo con un verbo. Luego, escribe una oración para cada par de sustantivo/verbo.

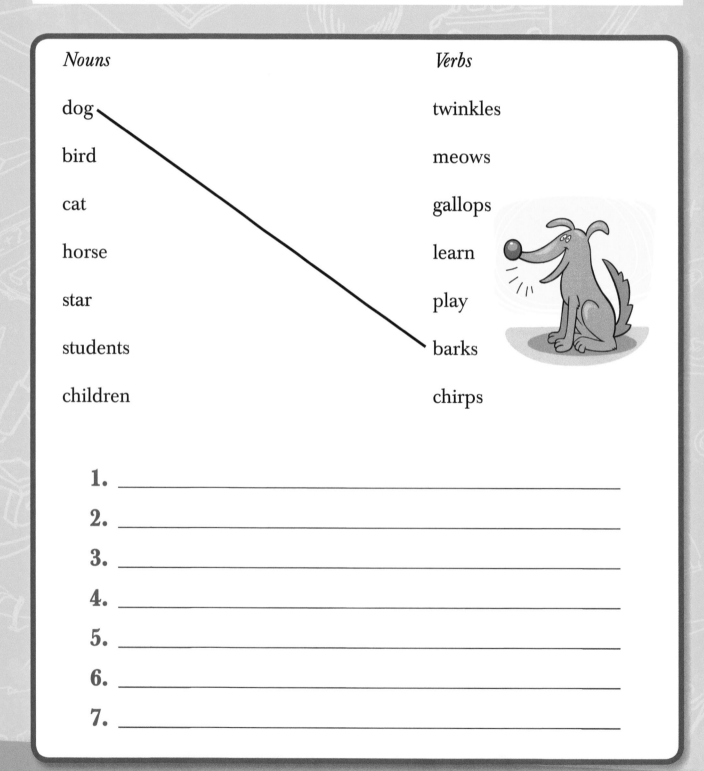

Nouns

dog

bird

cat

horse

star

students

children

Verbs

twinkles

meows

gallops

learn

play

barks

chirps

1. _____

2. _____

3. _____

4. _____

5. _____

6. _____

7. _____

Blotty Bother!

Directions: Rewrite each equation to include the missing digits. Then, solve each problem.

Instrucciones: Reescribe cada ecuación para incluir los dígitos que faltan. Luego, resuelve cada problema.

Elsa dropped ink all over her homework. Help her figure out which numbers are covered by the inkblots.

Elsa tiró tinta por toda su tarea. Ayúdala a deducir cuáles números están cubiertos por las manchas de tinta.

1. $4 \clubsuit + 3 = 44$ <u>   41 + 3 = 44   </u>

2. $\clubsuit + 19 = 27$ <u>   </u>

3. $22 - \clubsuit = 15$ <u>   </u>

4. $6 \clubsuit - 6 = 55$ <u>   </u>

5. $5 \clubsuit - 4 = 46$ <u>   </u>

6. $\clubsuit - 25 = 66$ <u>   </u>

7. $59 + \clubsuit 0 = 99$ <u>   </u>

8. $47 + \clubsuit \clubsuit = 69$ <u>   </u>

Word Find

Directions: Rearrange the letters on each bubble to spell short *u* words. Find and circle the words in the puzzle.

Instrucciones: *Vuelve a ordenar las letras de cada burbuja para formar palabras con el sonido "corto" de la* u. *Encuentra las palabras en el rompecabezas y enciérralas con un círculo.*

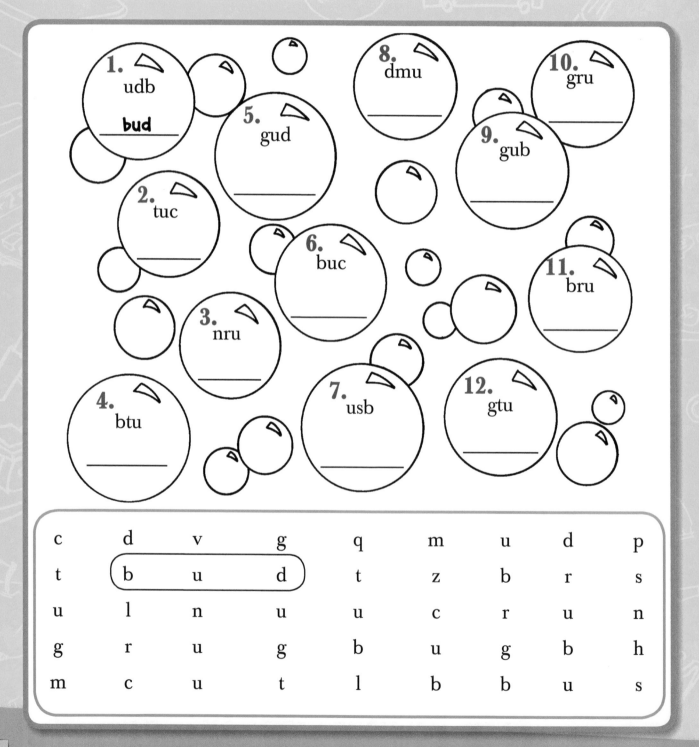

Story Problems

Directions: Write a number sentence to solve each story problem. Draw a picture on a separate sheet of paper to help you solve the problems.

Instrucciones: Escribe una oración numérica para resolver cada problema que se plantea. Haz un dibujo en otra hoja de papel para ayudarte a resolver el problema.

1. Crystal has a rock collection of 47 different types of rocks. She gave her friend Sara some rocks so she could start a collection. Crystal now has 38 rocks in her collection. How many rocks did she give Sara?

Number sentence:

_____

Answer:

_____

3. Brandon counted 51 vehicles on the drive to visit his grandfather. Fourteen of the 51 vehicles were motorcycles. How many of the 51 vehicles that Brandon counted were not motorcycles?

Number sentence:

_____

Answer:

_____

2. Kareena and Jade had 65 boxes of Girl Scout cookies to sell on Saturday. At the end of the day, they still had 14 boxes of cookies. How many boxes of cookies did they sell?

Number sentence:

_____

Answer:

_____

4. Mrs. Nunez's students brought in 36 science projects for display. After some students took their projects home, there were 28 left. How many projects were taken home?

Number sentence:

_____

Answer:

_____

Ready to Research

Directions: Choose a topic that you would like to learn more about, such as an animal, a planet, or a different country. Have your parent help you research the topic using the Internet, encyclopedias, or nonfiction books. Then, write a paragraph that includes new facts you learned.

Instrucciones: *Escoge un tema sobre el cual quisieras aprender más, como un animal, un planeta o un país diferente. Pide a tus padres que te ayuden a investigar el tema usando la Internet, enciclopedias o libros de no ficción. Luego, escribe un párrafo que incluye la nueva información que aprendiste.*

Teeth to Spare!

Directions: Read the article. Then, answer the questions.

Instrucciones: *Lee el artículo. Luego, contesta las preguntas.*

Shark Attack

Sharks have a lot of teeth. Most sharks have five rows of teeth. They do not use their teeth to chew like you do. They use them to tear their food into pieces. The first row is the largest. Each row gets smaller. When a tooth breaks, a new one takes its place. The new tooth does not come up from underneath like your teeth. The new tooth moves forward from the row behind it. A new one grows in the back row. A new tooth can grow in less than two weeks. A shark can have more than 30,000 teeth in its lifetime!

1. Write two facts about shark teeth.

   _____

   _____

   _____

2. Why did the author write about shark teeth?

   Ⓐ to tell about the shapes of shark teeth

   Ⓑ to tell about what sharks eat with their teeth

   Ⓒ to tell how sharks use and replace their teeth

Favorite Fruits Graph

Directions: Look at the results of a survey on favorite fruits. Then, make a bar graph to show the data. Be sure to label the graph correctly and give your graph a title.

Instrucciones: *Mira los resultados de una encuesta de frutas favoritas. Luego, haz una gráfica de barras para mostrar la información. Asegúrate de etiquetar cada parte de la gráfica correctamente y da un título a la gráfica.*

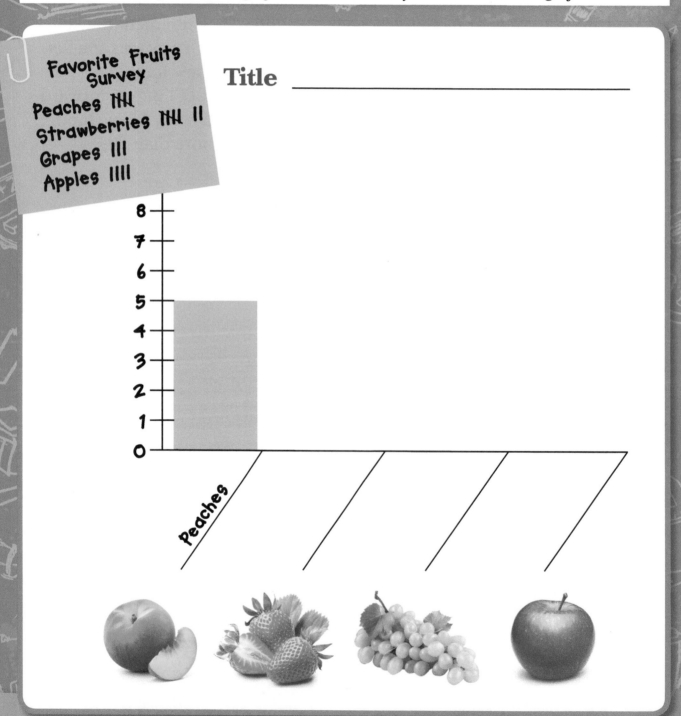

Favorite Fruits Survey

Peaches IIIII
Strawberries IIIII II
Grapes III
Apples IIII

Title _____

8
7
6
5
4
3
2
1
0

Peaches

Which Meaning?

Directions: Choose the meaning of the word as it is used in each sentence. Write the letter of the meaning used on the line next to each sentence.

Instrucciones: *Escoge el significado de la palabra de acuerdo a cómo se usa en cada oración. Escribe la letra del significado que se ha usado en la línea al lado de cada oración.*

part
A. a role in a play
B. a piece of a whole
C. divide

1. I will take <u>part</u> of the pizza. _____ B

2. Where do you <u>part</u> your hair? _____

3. The actress played the <u>part</u> of the mother. _____

4. Are you missing <u>part</u> of the puzzle? _____

5. My <u>part</u> in the skit is small. _____

cross
A. intersect
B. move from one side to another
C. angry

6. The highways <u>cross</u> in the north. _____

7. It's important to look for cars before you <u>cross</u> the street. _____

8. The child missed his nap and is feeling <u>cross</u>. _____

9. What are you so <u>cross</u> about? _____

10. Where do the lines of the letter T <u>cross</u>? _____

Telling Time

Directions: Choose the correct time for each clock.

Instrucciones: Escoge la hora correcta para cada reloj.

1.

- (A) 12:03
- (B) 3:12
- (C) 12:15
- (D) 12:45

3.

- (A) 10:05
- (B) 10:25
- (C) 11:30
- (D) 5:10

2.

- (A) 6:50
- (B) 8:10
- (C) 10:08
- (D) 7:45

4.

- (A) 9:15
- (B) 3:09
- (C) 9:03
- (D) 2:45

Be a Long Vowel Detective!

Directions: Choose the correct spelling for each word and write it on the blank.

Instrucciones: *Escoge la ortografía correcta para cada palabra y escríbela en el espacio en blanco.*

A Busy Day

Jack and Maria wanted to take a __boat_____ (boat/bote) ride. It

started to _____ (rane/rain). The thunder made a lot of

_____ (noyse/noise). "What can we do?" Jack asked their

mother. She told them that they should fill up a _____

(pail/pale) with _____ (hae/hay) to feed the horse. Then

they could _____ (plae/play) in the barn where it is

_____ (drie/dry).

Jack and Maria fed the horse. They

combed its _____ (tale/

tail). They helped their dad feed the

_____ (gote/goat). Soon,

the sun was out. They put up the

_____ (sale/sail) on the boat.

They had a great ride!

Add the Columns

Directions: Count the objects in each column below. Then, find the total number of objects.

Instrucciones: Cuenta los objetos en cada columna de abajo. Luego, encuentra el número total de objetos.

1.

$\underline{3} + \underline{3} + \underline{3} + \underline{3} = \underline{12}$

2.

___ + ___ + ___ + ___ = ___

3.

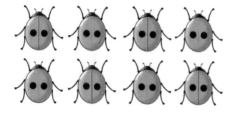

___ + ___ + ___ + ___ = ___

4.

___ + ___ + ___ = ___

5.

___ + ___ = ___

6.

___ + ___ + ___ = ___

#13535—*Kids Learn! Getting Ready for 3rd Grade*

Prefix Practice

Directions: Find the words with prefixes in the following sentences and underline them. Write the prefix, root word, and definition in the correct column. Use a dictionary to help if you need it.

Instrucciones: *Encuentra las palabras que tienen prefijos en las siguientes oraciones y subráyalas. Escribe el prefijo, la raíz de la palabra y la definición en la columna correcta. Usa un diccionario si lo necesitas.*

Sentence	Prefix	Root	Definition
1. Felix <u>reread</u> the book because it was good.	re	read	read again
2. Leila dialed an incorrect phone number.			
3. Does your sister go to preschool?			
4. Tyler was careful not to misspell any words on the test.			
5. Gina will unpack her suitcase when she gets home.			
6. In health class, we learned not to overeat.			
7. The character in the story was dishonest.			
8. Jose was unhappy when his team lost.			

Subtraction Action

Directions: Solve each problem.

Instrucciones: *Resuelve cada problema.*

1.
$$744 - 732$$

5.
$$367 - 130$$

9.
$$899 - 459$$

2.
$$980 - 950$$

6.
$$691 - 540$$

10.
$$288 - 231$$

3.
$$258 - 100$$

7.
$$917 - 714$$

11.
$$367 - 364$$

4.
$$484 - 373$$

8.
$$648 - 346$$

12.
$$776 - 203$$

How Would You Describe It?

Directions: Write a describing word (adjective) in each blank. You may want to use a thesaurus to improve your word choice.

Instrucciones: Escribe una palabra descriptiva (adjetivo) en cada espacio en blanco. Puedes usar un tesauro para mejorar tus opciones de palabras.

1. The _____ children ate ice cream.

2. A _____ puppy ran through the yard.

3. I like the _____ bike.

4. We can play with this _____ toy.

5. I am wearing a _____ pair of shoes.

6. My friend is _____.

7. The _____ nurse gave me a bandage.

8. I saw a _____ show on television.

9. There was a _____ spider hanging from its web.

10. The _____ pig rolled in the mud.

Batter Up!

Directions: Add the bats and baseballs. Then, decide whether the total is odd or even. Circle the correct word.

Instrucciones: Suma los bates y las pelotas de béisbol. Luego, decide si el total es impar o par. Encierra con un círculo la palabra correcta.

1.

   _3_

+ _3_

= _6_

odd   (even)

4.

   ___

+ ___

= ___

odd   even

2.

____

+ ___

= ___

odd   even

5.

____

+ ___

= ___

odd   even

3.

 ____

+ ___

= ___

odd   even

6.

____

+ ___

= ___

odd   even

Favorite Holiday

Directions: What is your favorite holiday? Write a paragraph about it. Be sure to use descriptive words.

Instrucciones: ¿Cuál es tu día festivo favorito? Escribe un párrafo sobre él. Asegúrate de usar palabras descriptivas.

Beginning: In a complete sentence, tell which holiday is your favorite.

_____

_____

Middle: Write 2–3 sentences telling why it is your favorite and how you and your family celebrate it.

_____

_____

_____

_____

Ending: Write one sentence repeating the name of your favorite holiday and how you feel about it.

_____

_____

Nonfiction Book

Directions: Choose a book that is nonfiction. That means it is about real things in the world around us. Before you read the book, fill out the first column below. After you read the book, complete the second column.

Instrucciones: *Escoge un libro de no ficción. Eso quiere decir que se trata de cosas reales en el mundo a nuestro alrededor. Antes de leer el libro, llena la primera columna de abajo. Después de leer el libro, completa la segunda columna.*

Book Title: _____

What is the book about? _____

Why did you choose this book? _____

_____

List 5 facts that you know about this subject.	List 5 facts that you learned by reading this book.
1. _____ _____	1. _____ _____
2. _____ _____	2. _____ _____
3. _____ _____	3. _____ _____
4. _____ _____	4. _____ _____
5. _____ _____	5. _____ _____

Part-Whole Practice

Directions: Complete the diagrams below to show the part-whole relationship of the numbers. Then, write one addition and one subtraction number sentence for each diagram. Work to memorize these sums.

Instrucciones: *Completa los diagramas de abajo para mostrar la relación entre las partes y el entero de los números. Luego, escribe una oración numérica de suma y una de resta para cada diagrama. Esfuérzate para memorizar estas sumas.*

 **Tip**

This diagram represents how a number can be made up of two parts:

Este diagrama representa cómo un número puede estar compuesto de dos partes:

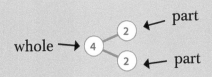
whole → 4 → part 2, part 2

1.

8, 3, 5

5 + 3 = 8

8 − 3 = 5

2.
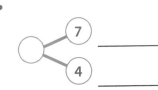
7, 4

_____

_____

3.

14, 8, ___

_____

_____

4.

9, 5

_____

_____

5.

16, 7, ___

_____

_____

6.

7, 8

_____

_____

7. On another sheet of paper, draw your own part-whole diagram. Write two number sentences for your diagram.

Pronoun Choices

Directions: Choose the correct pronoun from the Word Bank. Some pronouns are used more than once.

Instrucciones: *Escoge el pronombre correcto del Banco de palabras. Algunos pronombres se usan más de una vez.*

Word Bank

itself   myself   themselves   yourself

1. You should give _____**yourself**_____ a bath.

2. The kids got _____ some milk.

3. The ship crashed _____ on the rocks.

4. They brought snacks for _____.

5. I did my homework by _____.

6. Can you make breakfast by _____?

7. The bug climbed by _____ up the wall.

8. Can I get the book by _____?

Fun with Word Problems

Directions: Read each word problem. Solve each problem and write a number sentence for each.

Instrucciones: *Lee cada problema que se plantea. Resuelve cada problema y escribe una oración numérica para cada uno.*

1. Farmer Cole picked 93 bushels of apples. Farmer Dale picked 68 bushels. Find the sum of the bushels they picked.

$$\begin{array}{r} \overset{1}{9}3 \\ +68 \\ \hline 161 \end{array}$$

93 + 68 = 161

3. Dennis scored 43 points in his basketball game. Claire scored 40. What is the difference in points each earned?

2. Jason bought a pair of shoes for 53 dollars. Clark bought a pair for 28 dollars. What is the difference paid?

4. Jill counted 83 ants near an anthill. Jack counted 62. How many ants did they count altogether?

Look It Up

Directions: Use a dictionary to check the spellings of the underlined words. Mark the box to show whether a word is spelled correctly or incorrectly. If it is spelled incorrectly, write its correct spelling.

Instrucciones: Usa un diccionario para verificar la ortografía de cada una de las palabras subrayadas. Marca el cuadro que muestra si una palabra está escrita correctamente o incorrectamente. Si está escrita incorrectamente, escríbela correctamente.

	Correct	Incorrect	Correct Spelling
1. I am not <u>quiet</u> done with my sandwich.	☐	✔	quite
2. The boat <u>floted</u> smoothly over the water.	☐	☐	
3. The fast jet made a lot of <u>noise.</u>	☐	☐	
4. The children <u>laffed</u> at the clown.	☐	☐	
5. We went on an <u>exciting</u> trip.	☐	☐	
6. Please <u>wrapp</u> this gift.	☐	☐	
7. My <u>friend</u> asked me to play checkers.	☐	☐	
8. Lily put her <u>close</u> in the dryer.	☐	☐	

Break It Up

Directions: Find the area of each rectangle. Divide each rectangle into equal squares and count them to find the number of square units.

Instrucciones: *Encuentra el área de cada rectángulo. Divide cada rectángulo en cuadrados iguales y cuéntalos para encontrar el número de unidades cuadradas.*

1.

____**6**____ square units

4.

_____ square units

2.

_____ square units

5.

_____ square units

3.

_____ square units

6.

_____ square units

Compound Words

Directions: Combine two words from the Word Bank to make compound words. Write the meaning of each word on the line next to it.

Instrucciones: *Combina dos palabras del Banco de palabras para hacer palabras compuestas. Escribe el significado de cada palabra en la línea de al lado.*

 **Tip**

A *compound word* is made up of two smaller words. For example, *railroad* consists of two words, *rail* and *road*.

Una palabra compuesta *está hecha de dos palabras más cortas. Por ejemplo,* railroad *consiste de dos palabras,* rail *y* road.

Word Bank

day	play	rattle	moon	week
road	boat	snake	ground	rain
rail	sail	birth	end	light
bow	head	night	over	board

1. __birthday__   the day someone was born

2. _____ _____

3. _____ _____

4. _____ _____

5. _____ _____

6. _____ _____

7. _____ _____

8. _____ _____

9. _____ _____

10. _____ _____

Adding It Up

Directions: Solve the problems. *Hint:* You will need to regroup with some problems.

Instrucciones: *Resuelve los problemas.* Pista: *Tendrás que reagrupar en algunos de los problemas.*

1.
$$\begin{array}{r} {}^{1}26 \\ 33 \\ + 63 \\ \hline \mathbf{122} \end{array}$$

4.
$$\begin{array}{r} 27 \\ 13 \\ + 61 \\ \hline \end{array}$$

7.
$$\begin{array}{r} 10 \\ 58 \\ + 36 \\ \hline \end{array}$$

10.
$$\begin{array}{r} 44 \\ 46 \\ + 23 \\ \hline \end{array}$$

2.
$$\begin{array}{r} 66 \\ 45 \\ + 21 \\ \hline \end{array}$$

5.
$$\begin{array}{r} 72 \\ 46 \\ + 33 \\ \hline \end{array}$$

8.
$$\begin{array}{r} 64 \\ 64 \\ + 64 \\ \hline \end{array}$$

11.
$$\begin{array}{r} 58 \\ 41 \\ + 18 \\ \hline \end{array}$$

3.
$$\begin{array}{r} 90 \\ 26 \\ + \ 6 \\ \hline \end{array}$$

6.
$$\begin{array}{r} 38 \\ 33 \\ + 81 \\ \hline \end{array}$$

9.
$$\begin{array}{r} 45 \\ 31 \\ + 14 \\ \hline \end{array}$$

12.
$$\begin{array}{r} 58 \\ 11 \\ + 23 \\ \hline \end{array}$$

The Milkmaid and her Pail

Directions: Read the story. Then, answer the questions.

Instrucciones: Lee la historia. Luego, contesta las preguntas.

I am Patty, the milkmaid. One morning I was going to market, carrying my milk in a pail on my head. As I went along, I thought about what I would do with the money I would get for the milk.

"I'll buy some chickens from Farmer Brown," I thought to myself. "The chickens will lay eggs each morning, which I will sell to the parson's wife. With the money that I get from the sale of these eggs, I'll buy myself a fancy frock and a chip hat. When I go to market, won't all the young men come up and speak to me! Polly Shaw will be jealous, but I won't care. I shall just look at her and toss my head like this."

But then disaster happened. As I tossed my head back, the pail fell off. The milk spilled all over the ground.

I had to go home and tell my mother what had happened.

"Ah, my child," my mother said. "Do not count your chickens before they are hatched."

1. A *moral* is a lesson. What is the moral of this story?

_____

_____

2. Tell about a time when you "counted your chickens before they had hatched."

_____

_____

_____

Jumping on a Number Line

Directions: Show each sum or difference on an open number line. You may make several jumps of ten or one single jump to show the addition or subtraction.

Instrucciones: *Muestra cada suma o diferencia en una línea numérica vacía. Puedes dar varios saltos de diez o un solo salto para mostrar la suma o la resta.*

Tip

An open number line can be a helpful model of addition and subtraction. Start with one *addend* and jump to the right when adding. Start with the *minuend* and jump to the left when subtracting. Make sure the jump is the right size.

Una línea numérica vacía puede ser un modelo útil de sumas y restas. Empieza con un sumando y salta a la derecha al sumar. Empieza con un minuendo y salta a la izquierda al restar. Asegúrate de que el salto sea del tamaño correcto.

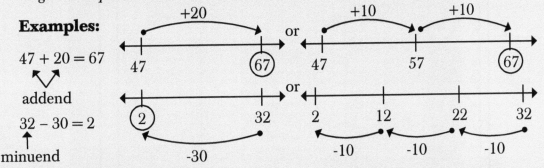

Examples:

$47 + 20 = 67$

addend

$32 - 30 = 2$

minuend

---

1. $14 + 50 =$ _____ **64** _____

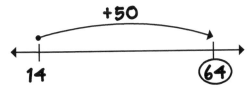

2. $72 + 10 =$ _____

3. $55 - 20 =$ _____

4. $63 + 30 =$ _____

5. $84 - 40 =$ _____

6. $46 - 20 =$ _____

Wish You Were Here!

Directions: Pretend you are away on vacation. Write a postcard to your best friend and tell him or her about your trip.

Instrucciones: Imagina que estás de vacaciones. Escríbele una postal a tu mejor amigo o amiga y cuéntale de tu viaje.

The Water Cycle

Directions: Look at the diagram. Then, answer the questions.

Instrucciones: Mira el diagrama. Luego, contesta las preguntas.

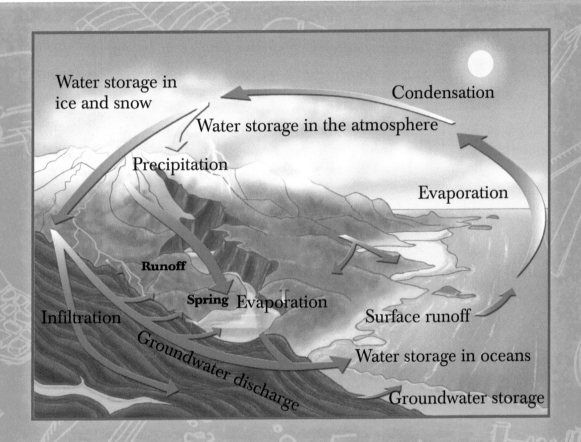

1. How does the diagram help you understand the water cycle?

_____

_____

_____

2. List one question that you have about something in the diagram.

_____

_____

_____

Length Detective

Directions: Find 5 small objects. Use a ruler to measure their lengths in centimeters (cm). Record their lengths on the chart. On a separate sheet of paper, make a line plot to show the lengths you found.

Instrucciones: *Encuentra 5 objetos pequeños. Usa una regla para medir sus longitudes en centímetros (cm). Registra sus longitudes en la gráfica. En otra hoja de papel, haz una gráfica de puntos para mostrar las longitudes que encontraste.*

Tip

A *line plot* is a diagram that shows how frequently something occurs. The *X* above a number in a line plot stands for one piece of data. The example below shows the length of 8 objects.

Una gráfica de puntos es un diagrama que muestra qué tan frecuentemente ocurre algo. La X sobre un número en una gráfica de puntos representa un dato. El ejemplo de abajo muestra la longitud de 8 objetos.

Example:

```
                              X
                              X       X
          X           X       X       X       X
          10    11    12    13    14    15
```
Lengths of Objects (in centimeters)

Object	Length
1.	_____ cm
2.	_____ cm
3.	_____ cm
4.	_____ cm
5.	_____ cm

Find the Noun

Directions: Underline the nouns in the sentence.

Instrucciones: *Subraya los sustantivos de cada oración.*

A *noun* names a person, place, thing, or idea.
Un sustantivo *nombra una persona, un lugar, una cosa o una idea.*

person   place   thing   idea

1. The <u>dancer</u> jumped in the <u>air</u>.

2. The boy watched television.

3. Mr. Smith teaches our class.

4. The baby cried for her mother.

5. The sisters walked to the store.

6. My school has six buildings.

7. The teenagers rode their skateboards through the park.

8. The dentist treated a new patient.

9. A little dog picked a fight with a big cat.

10. There were presents, cake, and candles at my birthday party.

What Big Numbers!

Directions: Draw number disks to show each number. Then, write the number in expanded form.

Instrucciones: *Dibuja discos de números para mostrar cada número. Luego, escribe el número en forma desarrollada.*

1.

Hundreds	Tens	Ones
(100)(100) (100)(100)(100) (100)(100)	(10)(10) (10) (10)	(1) (1)

742

____700____ + ____40____ + ____2____ = ____742____

2.

Hundreds	Tens	Ones

87

_____ + _____ + _____ = _____

3.

Hundreds	Tens	Ones

999

_____ + _____ + _____ = _____

Vowel Teams

Directions: List words that have the following vowel teams and sounds.

Instrucciones: *Escribe palabras que tengan los siguientes grupos de vocales y sonidos.*

ai (Long A)	**ay (Long A)**	**ea (Long E)**
braid	_____	_____
rain	_____	_____
_____	_____	_____
_____	_____	_____
_____	_____	_____

ee (Long E)	**ie (Long E)**	**ie (Long I)**
_____	_____	_____
_____	_____	_____
_____	_____	_____
_____	_____	_____
_____	_____	_____

oa (Long O)	**ou ("ow" sound)**	**oo (Long U)**
_____	_____	_____
_____	_____	_____
_____	_____	_____
_____	_____	_____

Marble Division

Directions: Divide the marbles into equal groups. Then, complete the division problem.

Instrucciones: Divide las canicas en grupos iguales. Luego, completa el problema de división.

1. Divide 12 into groups of 3. $12 \div 3 = \underline{\quad 4 \quad}$

2. Divide 20 into groups of 5. $20 \div 5 = \underline{\qquad}$

3. Divide 44 into groups of 11. $44 \div 11 = \underline{\qquad}$

4. Divide 30 into groups of 6. $30 \div 6 = \underline{\qquad}$

5. Divide 100 into groups of 10. $100 \div 10 = \underline{\qquad}$

13535—Kids Learn! Getting Ready for 3rd Grade

What Do You Think?

Directions: There are 7 incomplete sentences below. Rewrite the sentences to make them complete.

Instrucciones: *Hay 7 oraciones incompletas abajo. Reescribe las oraciones para que estén completas.*

Tip

A sentence needs to have enough information to make sense. It needs to ask a complete question or tell a complete idea.

Una oración debe contener la información suficiente para que tenga sentido. Debe formar una pregunta completa o indicar una idea completa.

1. Jennifer wants to

_____

2. Yesterday, while it was raining, I

_____

3. Do you

_____

4. all the way down the hill

_____

5. is very annoying

_____

6. I wish I had

_____

7. Did they try

_____

Use a Bar Model

Directions: Draw a bar model to help you solve each problem. Then, write a number sentence for the problem. Answer the question in a complete sentence.

Instrucciones: *Dibuja un modelo de barras para ayudarte a resolver cada problema. Luego, escribe una oración numérica para el problema. Contesta la pregunta con una oración completa.*

A *bar model* is a diagram used for solving word problems. It can be very helpful for organizing and visualizing information. The top number represents the whole amount. The bar is divided into pieces of different sizes to show parts of the whole.

Un modelo de barras *es un diagrama que se usa para resolver problemas de planteo. Puede ser muy útil para organizar y visualizar información. El número de arriba representa la cantidad entera. La barra se divide en secciones de diferentes tamaños para mostrar partes de un entero.*

Example:
Ramon had 6 toy cars. Then, he bought 9 more. How many toy cars does he have now?

$6 + 9 = ?$
Ramon has 15 cars.

1. Mr. Britton drives a bus. On Monday, he picked up 12 passengers at the first stop. At the second stop, he picked up some more passengers. Then, he had 20 passengers. How many passengers did Mr. Britton pick up at the second stop?

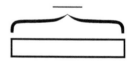

2. On Tuesday, Mr. Britton picked up 11 passengers at the first stop. He picked up 6 more passengers at the second stop. How many passengers were on the bus after the second stop?

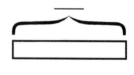

Caring for a Pet

Directions: Read the passage, then answer the questions.

Instrucciones: Lee el pasaje, luego contesta las siguientes preguntas.

Do you have a pet? If not, maybe you will want to get a goldfish. A goldfish is a pet that many people have. It's very easy to take care of a goldfish!

If you have a bowl and water, you have a home for a goldfish! Make sure you keep the water clean.

Then, you will need to feed your goldfish. They can eat plants and other things. But, you can buy fish food at a pet store. Goldfish like this just as much!

Now that you can **take** care of a goldfish, you can pick one out! Goldfish come in many colors. They can be red or gold. They can be brown or black.

Fluency Goal: Read 90 words in one minute. The bolded word is the 90th word in the passage.
Meta para la fluidez: Leer 90 palabras en un minuto. La palabra en negrita es la palabra número 90 en la historia.

1. What can you feed a goldfish?

_____

_____

2. What colors do goldfish come in?

_____

_____

3. Would you like to have a goldfish as a pet? Why or why not?

_____

_____

Be a Math Teacher

Directions: Make up a word problem and write it on the lines below. Then, explain how to solve your word problem. You may use pictures, numbers, and words to show how to solve the problem.

Instrucciones: *Inventa un problema de planteo y escríbelo en las líneas de abajo. Luego, explica cómo resolver tu problema de planteo. Puedes usar imágenes, números y palabras para mostrar cómo resolver el problema.*

Word Problem

_____

_____

_____

_____

_____

How to Solve the Problem

Choose Your Own Adventure

Directions: Be creative! Make up a story with unique characters and a fun plot. Write a draft of your story on a separate sheet of paper. Ask an adult to help you edit and proofread your writing. Then, complete your final draft on the lines below.

Instrucciones: *¡Sé creativo! Inventa una historia con personajes únicos y una trama divertida. Escribe un borrador de tu historia en una hoja de papel aparte. Pide a un adulto que te ayude a editar y revisar tu escritura. Luego, completa tu borrador final en las líneas de abajo.*

Preparing Your Child for Assessments

Background for Parents

The Every Student Succeeds Act (ESSA) mandates that all states adopt challenging academic standards that help students meet the goal of college and career readiness. While many states adopted academic standards prior to ESSA, the act continues to hold states accountable for detailed and comprehensive standards.

Standards are designed to focus instruction. They define the knowledge, skills, and content students should acquire at each level. Standards are also used to develop standardized assessments to evaluate students' academic progress.

Standardized assessments include a variety of types of items. Some items ask students to select the correct option or options from a list. Other items ask students to give a written or numerical response. Students will also complete tasks that gauge their ability to bring together knowledge and skills across many standards.

Preparation Pages

The test preparation items on pages 88–102 provide sample test questions and tasks similar to those that may be found on next-generation assessments. Use the following tips to work through the assessment practice pages with your child:

- Work with your child as he or she completes the practice items so that you can address any questions as they arise.

- Help your child understand how to go about selecting answers or working through tasks.

- Use the Answer Key to check the answers together, and discuss any incorrect responses.

- Keep in mind that for the purposes of this practice, getting the correct answer is not as important as helping your child become comfortable with the test-taking format and process.

#13535—Kids Learn! Getting Ready for 3rd Grade

Preparar a su hijo para las evaluaciones

Información general para los padres

La Ley Cada Estudiante Triunfa (Every Student Succeeds Act), o ESSA por sus siglas en inglés, exige que cada estado adopte estándares educativos estimulantes que ayuden a los estudiantes a cumplir con el objetivo de estar preparados para la universidad y para el trabajo. Aunque muchos estados adoptaron estándares educativos antes de ESSA, esta ley hace responsables a los estados de implementar estándares detallados y comprensivos.

Los estándares están diseñados para guiar la enseñanza. Definen el conocimiento, las destrezas y el contenido que los estudiantes deben aprender en cada nivel. Los estándares también se usan para desarrollar evaluaciones estandarizadas con las que se evalúa el progreso académico de los estudiantes.

Las evaluaciones estandarizadas incluyen una variedad de tipos de problemas. Algunos problemas les piden a los estudiantes que escojan la opción correcta u opciones de una lista. Otros problemas les piden a los estudiantes que den una respuesta escrita o numérica. Los estudiantes también completarán tareas que miden su habilidad para unir el conocimiento y las destrezas de muchos estándares.

Páginas de preparación para pruebas

Los problemas de preparación para pruebas en las páginas 88–102 proveen ejemplos de preguntas de pruebas y tareas similares a las que puedan encontrarse en las evaluaciones. Use los siguientes consejos para completar las páginas de preparación para pruebas con su hijo:

- Trabaje junto con su hijo mientras completa los problemas de práctica para que cuando surja cualquier pregunta pueda tratar con ella.

- Ayude a su hijo a entender cómo escoger las respuestas o completar las tareas.

- Use la Hoja de respuestas para juntos revisar las respuestas y analizar cualquier respuesta incorrecta.

- Tenga en cuenta que para los propósitos de esta práctica, obtener la respuesta correcta no es tan importante como ayudar a que su hijo se sienta cómodo con el formato y el proceso de evaluación.

Language Arts Assessment Practice

Directions: Read the passage below. Then, answer the questions on page 89.

Wild Again

In the country of Mongolia, there once lived wild horses. Mongolia is in Asia. That's next to China. The horses are called Takhi. They used to roam the plains. Then about 50 years ago, the wild horses died out. Hunters had killed some of them. Others died because their lands were used for farming or towns.

By 1960, the only Takhi left were in three zoos in different parts of the world. Scientists decided to try to save the Takhi. They began studying how to help the horses survive. They decided to try to bring wild horses back to Mongolia.

In 1992, Takhi that had been born in zoos were sent to Mongolia. Sixteen horses left the zoos for their new home. The horses were put in special areas. Hunters were kept away. The horses were given plenty of room. By 2006, there were over 300 wild Takhi. Some of them were born in the wild.

The San Diego Zoo's Wild Animal Park in California is one of the zoos that helped. They sent Takhi from their herd to Mongolia. Oliver Ryder is a scientist who works with the San Diego horses. He says the wild horses will make it, if we help them. "It's up to people," he says. "If we give the Takhi enough space, they will survive."

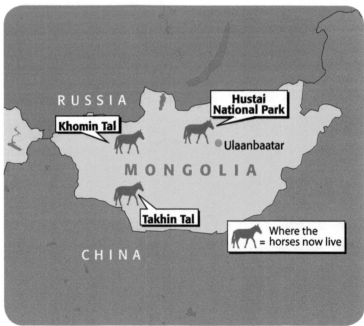

This map shows the special areas
where wild horses live in Mongolia.

Language Arts Assessment Practice (cont.)

1. Reread the first paragraph of "Wild Again." Underline the sentence that shows the main idea.

> In the country of Mongolia, there once lived wild horses. Mongolia is in Asia. That's next to China. The horses are called Takhi. They used to roam the plains. Then about 50 years ago, the wild horses died out. Hunters had killed some of them. Others died because their lands were used for farming or towns.

2. Why did the wild horses disappear? Fill in the bubble next to all correct answers.

   (A) "The horses are called Takhi."

   (B) "Hunters had killed some of them."

   (C) "Mongolia is in Asia."

   (D) "Others died because their lands were used for farming or towns."

Directions: Read the passage below. Then, answer the questions below and on page 91.

The Life of Helen Keller

Helen Keller was born in 1880. She was a healthy baby. The first year of her life was normal. One day, she had a very high fever. She got really sick. She lost her sight. She also lost her hearing. She was blind and deaf.

Helen grew very frustrated. She could not hear. She could not see. She could not talk to people. Helen began to have horrible tantrums.

Helen's family needed help. They hired a teacher. Anne Sullivan became Helen's teacher. She taught Helen many things. She taught her new words. She helped Helen connect ideas. This helped Helen learn to speak. She was six years old. She felt Anne's lips as she talked. Helen copied Anne. Anne was not always easy to understand. Yet Helen never gave up.

Helen worked hard her entire life. She grew to be an amazing woman. She went to college. She wrote books. She traveled the world. She did not let anything stop her.

Perhaps Helen's greatest gift was teaching others to respect her. She wanted respect for all people who are blind or deaf. She shared her life with others. Helen Keller died in 1968. She lived a full life. She was a hero to many people.

3. What happened to Helen Keller when she was young?

_____

_____

_____

_____

_____

Language Arts Assessment Practice *(cont.)*

4. Write the numbers 1, 2, 3, and 4 in the boxes to show the order of events in Helen Keller's life.

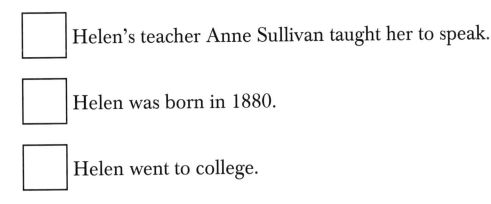

☐ Helen's teacher Anne Sullivan taught her to speak.

☐ Helen was born in 1880.

☐ Helen went to college.

☐ Helen got very sick and became blind and deaf.

---

5. Draw a line to match the words from the passage with those similar in meaning.

frustrated	whole
horrible	terrible
entire	value
respect	upset

Language Arts Assessment Practice *(cont.)*

Directions: Read the paragraph below. Then, answer the questions below.

> Brady really wanted to learn how to ride his bike. All of his friends were able to ride bikes, and he felt excluded. They never invited him to play anymore. Brady had been trying all summer. He was not having much luck. His dad suggested they go to the park. He thought the wide, open space would be helpful. He was right, and Brady rode right away!

6. Fill in the bubbles next to the sentence or sentences that help you understand the meaning of the word <u>excluded</u>.

   (A) "Brady really wanted to learn how to ride his bike."

   (B) "They never invited him to play anymore."

   (C) "He was not having much luck."

   (D) "He was right, and Brady rode right away!"

7. How did Brady feel about learning to ride his bike? What did he do?

   _____

   _____

   _____

   _____

Language Arts Assessment Practice (cont.)

8. Han is writing a paragraph. He needs to correct the punctuation mistakes in his paragraph. Read the paragraph. Underline the two sentences that do not have correct punctuation.

> I cant wait for school to start. I'll be in third grade this fall. Mr. Rodriguez will be my teacher. Ive heard that he is the best teacher at Washington Elementary.

9. Maribel is writing about her summer vacation. Read the paragraph. She wants to add one sentence to the end of her paragraph. Choose the best conclusion for the paragraph.

> This has been the best summer vacation of my life! I went swimming almost every day in my grandma's pool. I also got to go camping with my friend Su's family. I had lots of time to ride my bike and do art projects.

(A) I don't like winter as much as summer.

(B) I wish this summer would never end!

(C) I like the hot weather, too.

(D) Camping was really fun.

Language Arts Assessment Practice *(cont.)*

10. Shawn is proofreading the paragraph below. Help him by underlining the three spelling mistakes.

> Sean was going on a plan to visit his uncle. It was the first time he had ever ben on a plane alone. Sean was old enough to fly by himself. He knew which people to ask for help if he needed it. He had already met the flite attendants. His mom had packed a bag with games and snacks for the short trip. Sean smiled with satisfaction as he sat on the plane by himself, and he was ready to go!

11. Which of the plural nouns below is not correct? There may be more than one.

- (A) childs
- (B) feet
- (C) mice
- (D) tooths

12. Change the verbs in the box to the past tense to complete the sentences.

> sit   hide   tell   say

12a. I _____ my mom that I wanted a basketball for my birthday.

12b. Taline _____ on the bench while she waited for her friend.

12c. The scared kitten _____ under the bed.

12d. My brother _____ that he would like to visit China.

Language Arts Assessment Practice *(cont.)*

13. Finish the story below. Use words from the box to show the order
of events.

next	second	then	finally	lastly	after	that

Max wanted to build a fort in his room. First, he found some pillows.

_____

_____

_____

_____

_____

_____

_____

_____

_____

_____

_____

_____

_____

Mathematics Assessment Practice

Directions: Complete the assessment practice.

1. Fill in the bubble next to all equations that are true.

   (A) $545 + 100 = 645$

   (B) $812 - 10 = 822 + 10$

   (C) $373 + 10 = 473$

   (D) $401 - 100 = 311 - 10$

   (E) $293 + 10 = 303$

2. Peter drinks 4 cups of water every day. How many cups of water will he drink in 2 days? Explain how you solved this problem. Use pictures, numbers, and words.

Mathematics Assessment Practice *(cont.)*

3. Create a bar graph using the data in the tally chart.

Pets	Number of Students
dogs	ЖL
cats	IIII
birds	I
fish	II

4. Use the bar graph you made for item 3. How many more students chose dogs than chose cats?

Mathematics Assessment Practice *(cont.)*

5. Use the drawing below to answer the questions.

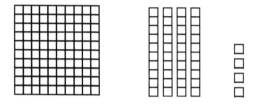

    5a. Write the numeral for the number above: _____

    5b. Write the number in expanded form: _____

    5c. Write the number in word form: _____

---

6. Compare the numbers using >, <, or =.

    6a. 774 $\bigcirc$ 477

    6b. 509 $\bigcirc$ 801

    6c. 110 $\bigcirc$ 191

Mathematics Assessment Practice *(cont.)*

7. Look at the drawing below. Choose all the number sentences that show the total.

- (A) $4 + 4 + 4 + 4 + 4 = 20$
- (B) $5 + 5 + 5 = 15$
- (C) $5 + 5 + 5 + 5 = 20$
- (D) $4 + 5 = 9$
- (E) $4 + 4 + 5 + 5 = 20$

---

8. Choose all the shapes that are hexagons.

- (A)
- (B)
- (C)
- (D)
- (E)

Mathematics Assessment Practice *(cont.)*

9. Choose all the figures that have one-third shaded.

(A)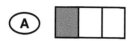

(B)

(C)

(D)

(E)

---

10. Solve the problem.

$87 - 48 = \boxed{}$

#13535—Kids Learn! Getting Ready for 3rd Grade

© *Teacher Created Materials*

Mathematics Assessment Practice *(cont.)*

11. Sonya earned $1.25 doing chores. Then, her dad gave her $0.50. How much money does Sonya have now?

---

12. Show 3:55 on the clock.

Mathematics Assessment Practice *(cont.)*

13. Circle odd or even for each set of pictures.

13a. ▲▲▲▲▲▲▲▲▲▲ odd even

13b. ●●●●●●● odd even

13c. ★★★★★★★★★★★★★★ odd even

---

14. Fill in the missing numbers on the number line.

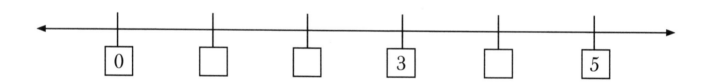

Great Work!

(Name)

has completed

Kids Learn! Getting Ready for 3rd Grade

(Date)

Answer Key

Page 20

1. th
2. ch
3. sh
4. th; sh
5. th; sh
6. ch
7. th
8. wh; th
9. sh; th
10. sh; ch; wh
11. ch
12. sh

Page 21

1. >
2. >
3. >
4. >
5. <
6. <
7. <
8. >
9. <
10. >
11. >
12. >
13. >
14. <
15. <

Page 22

1. ham-mer
2. let-ter
3. pil-low
4. win-dow
5. lad-der
6. num-bers
7. but-ter
8. mon-key
9. doc-tor

Page 23

1. 789
2. 877
3. 787
4. 986
5. 869
6. 796
7. 566
8. 899
9. 777
10. 989
11. 895
12. 778
13. 636
14. 339
15. 787
16. 889

Page 24

1. The
2. Freddy Wilson's; Peepers; Mrs. Woolsey's
3. The; Thursday; November; Thanksgiving
4. I; Halloween; Saturday
5. Aunt Susan; Yellowstone National Park
6. Connie; Maple Street; Bismarck; North Dakota
7. Brazil; Argentina; Peru; South America
8. The; Mediterranean Sea; Atlantic Ocean; Spain
9. The; Love; Esther
10. Davis Medical Center; January
11. We; Youko; Japan
12. Last; Tuesday; Ruben; Spotty; Tulip Street; Central Park

Page 25

1. 3
2. 5
3. 2
4. 4
5. 2
6. 3
7. 4
8. 3

Page 26

1. The cat chased the bird.
2. I wrote a letter to my friend.
3. The family took a trip.
4. The baker baked a cake.
5. A penguin jumped into the sea.
6. The puppets sang a song to the audience.

Page 27

1. 33 cents
2. 30 cents
3. 24 cents
4. $3.50
5. Answers will vary.

Page 28

Answers will vary.

Page 29

1. 4; 4; 4
2. 1; 9; 2
3. 6; 7; 6
4. 3; 4; 6
5.

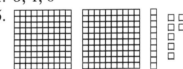

Page 30

Answers will vary.

Answer Key (cont.)

Page 31

1. Answers will vary. Possible answer: The main characters are both hardworking.
2. Answers will vary. Possible answer: The author shows the characters trying lots of ways to make money to go to the movies.
3. Answers will vary. Possible answer: The girls could have had a bake sale.

Page 32

1. 240
2. 915
3. 720
4. 250
5. 750
6. 365
7. 365
8. 660
9. 865
10. 970
11. 375
12. 380
13. Answers will vary. Possible answer: I add one to the hundreds place of the number and keep the digits in the tens and ones places the same.

Page 33

1. What's
2. it'll
3. they'd
4. there's
5. Who's
6. could've

Page 34

1. 778
2. 406
3. 233
4. 491
5. 700 + 60 + 5
6. 500 + 50 + 7
7. one hundred twenty-nine
8. three hundred sixty-five

Page 35

1. B
2. C

Page 36

1. 132
2. 115
3. 164
4. 121

Page 37

Answers will vary. Possible answer: My baby brother is a pest. He always makes a mess when he gets into my room. He got into my room yesterday while I was at school. First, he took all of the pages out of one of my books. Then, he made another mess by pulling out all the things I had hidden under the bed. He also got into my closet and pulled all my clothes off the hangers. He should never be allowed to go into my room. I want him locked out of my room forever!

Page 38

1. 310; 510
2. 430; 630; 730; 830
3. 140; 340; 440; 540
4. 570; 670; 770; 970
5. 480; 580; 680; 780
6. 190; 290; 390; 490
7. 415; 515; 615; 815
8. 199; 399; 499; 599
9. 101; 301; 401; 501
10. 233; 333; 433; 533

Page 39

1. blew
2. sang
3. wore
4. cried
5. made
6. fell
7. catch
8. ride
9. pay
10. sweep
11. read
12. take

Page 40

1. 17
2. 57
3. 17
4. 19

Page 41

Answers will vary.

Page 42

1. C
2. Jupiter

Answer Key (cont.)

Page 43

1. quadrilateral
2. hexagon
3. triangle
4. cube
5. pentagon
6. quadrilateral
7. Answers will vary, but shape should have five sides.
8. Students should draw a triangle.

Page 44

1. women
2. teeth
3. men
4. children
5. feet
6. mice
7. fish
8. wives
9. geese
10. loaves

Page 45

1. Answers will vary. Possible answer:

$6 \times 2 = 12$

2. Answers will vary. Possible answer:

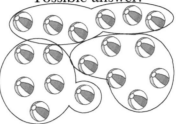

$3 \times 6 = 18$

3. Answers will vary. Possible answer:

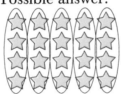

$5 \times 4 = 20$

4. Answers will vary. Possible answer:

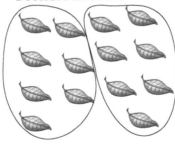

$2 \times 7 = 14$

Page 46

1. Answers will vary. Possible answer: Each student in the class got an award.
2. Answers will vary. Possible answer: The monkey was very full.
3. Answers will vary. Possible answer: The girl had to finish her homework during recess.
4. Answers will vary. Possible answer: There was a car accident on the highway.
5. Answers will vary. Possible answer: My sister bumped my ice cream cone.
6. Answers will vary. Possible answer: The baby was hungry.

Page 47

1. $\frac{1}{4}$; one-fourth
2. $\frac{2}{3}$; two-thirds
3. $\frac{1}{3}$; one-third
4. $\frac{1}{4}$; one-fourth
5. $\frac{3}{4}$; three-fourths
6. $\frac{1}{2}$; one-half

Page 48

Matching: dog, barks; bird, chirps; cat, meows; horse, gallops; star, twinkles; students, learn; children, play. Sentences will vary.

Page 49

1. $41 + 3 = 44$
2. $8 + 19 = 27$
3. $22 - 7 = 15$
4. $61 - 6 = 55$
5. $50 - 4 = 46$
6. $91 - 25 = 66$
7. $59 + 40 = 99$
8. $47 + 22 = 69$

Answer Key (cont.)

Page 50

1. bud
2. cut
3. run
4. tub/but
5. dug
6. cub
7. sub/bus
8. mud
9. bug
10. rug
11. rub
12. gut/tug

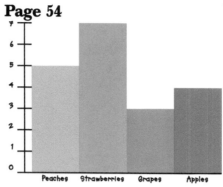

Page 51

1. 47 – ? = 38; Pictures will vary; Crystal gave Sara 9 rocks.
2. 65 – ? = 14; Pictures will vary; They sold 51 boxes of cookies.
3. 51 – 14 = ?; Pictures will vary; 37 vehicles were not motorcycles.
4. 36 – ? = 28; Pictures will vary; 8 projects were taken home.

Page 52

Answers will vary.

Page 53

1. Answers will vary. Possible answer: The first row of teeth is the largest. When a shark breaks a tooth, it grows a new one.
2. C

Page 54

Page 55

1. B
2. C
3. A
4. B
5. A
6. A
7. B
8. C
9. C
10. A

Page 56

1. C
2. A
3. B
4. A

Page 57

1. boat
2. rain
3. noise
4. pail
5. hay
6. play
7. dry
8. tail
9. goat
10. sail

Page 58

1. 3 + 3 + 3 + 3 = 12
2. 4 + 4 + 4 + 4 = 16
3. 2 + 2 + 2 + 2 = 8
4. 3 + 3 + 3 = 9
5. 5 + 5 = 10
6. 5 + 5 + 5 = 15

Page 59

1. reread; re; read; read again
2. incorrect; in; correct; not correct
3. preschool; pre; school; school children go to before kindergarten
4. misspell; mis; spell; spell wrong
5. unpack; un; pack; take things out of a packed bag
6. overeat; over; eat; eat too much
7. dishonest; dis; honest; not honest
8. unhappy; un; happy; not happy

Page 60

1. 12
2. 30
3. 158
4. 111
5. 237
6. 151
7. 203
8. 302
9. 440
10. 57
11. 3
12. 573

Page 61

Answers will vary, but all words should be adjectives.

Answer Key (cont.)

Page 62

1. $3 + 3 = 6$; even
2. $9 + 8 = 17$; odd
3. $6 + 9 = 15$; odd
4. $4 + 5 = 9$; odd
5. $4 + 4 = 8$; even
6. $10 + 9 = 19$; odd

Page 63

Answers will vary.

Page 64

Answers will vary.

Page 65

1. 5; Answers will vary.
   Possible answers: $5 + 3 = 8$; $8 - 3 = 5$
2. 11; Answers will vary.
   Possible answers: $7 + 4 = 11$; $11 - 7 = 4$
3. 6; Answers will vary.
   Possible answers: $8 + 6 = 14$; $14 - 8 = 6$
4. 14; Answers will vary.
   Possible answers: $9 + 5 = 14$; $14 - 5 = 9$
5. 9; Answers will vary.
   Possible answers: $9 + 7 = 16$; $16 - 7 = 9$
6. 15; Answers will vary.
   Possible answers: $7 + 8 = 15$; $15 - 7 = 8$
7. Answers will vary.

Page 66

1. yourself
2. themselves
3. itself
4. themselves
5. myself
6. yourself
7. itself
8. myself

Page 67

1. $93 + 68 = 161$
2. $53 - 28 = 25$
3. $43 - 40 = 3$
4. $83 + 62 = 145$

Page 68

1. incorrect; quite
2. incorrect; floated
3. correct
4. incorrect; laughed
5. correct
6. incorrect; wrap
7. correct
8. incorrect; clothes

Page 69

1. 6
2. 18
3. 24
4. 8
5. 5
6. 16

Page 70

Order will vary. Possible answers:

1. birthday; the day someone was born
2. sailboat; boat with sails
3. railroad; a road of rails for trains
4. headlight; the light at the front of a car
5. moonlight; light from the moon
6. rattlesnake; a snake with a rattle
7. rainbow; a colorful arch that appears after rain
8. weekday; day of the week
9. weekend; end of the week
10. playground; place to play

Page 71

1. 122
2. 132
3. 122
4. 101
5. 151
6. 152
7. 104
8. 192
9. 90
10. 113
11. 117
12. 92

Page 72

1. Answers will vary.
   Possible answer: The moral is not to count on something good happening in the future or you might be disappointed.
2. Answers will vary.

Page 73

1. $14 + 50 = 64$
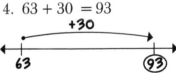
2. $72 + 10 = 82$
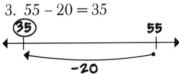
3. $55 - 20 = 35$
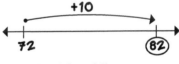
4. $63 + 30 = 93$
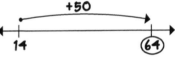
5. $84 - 40 = 44$
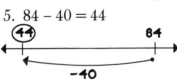
6. $46 - 20 = 26$
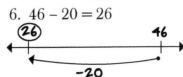

Answer Key (cont.)

Page 74

Answers will vary.

Page 75

Answers will vary.
  Possible answers:
1. The diagram shows how the different parts of the water cycle are connected.
2. What is infiltration?

Page 76

Answers will vary.

Page 77

1. dancer; air
2. boy; television
3. Mr. Smith; class
4. baby; mother
5. sisters; store
6. school; buildings
7. teenagers; skateboards; park
8. dentist; patient
9. dog; fight; cat
10. presents; cake; candles; party; birthday

Page 78

1. $700 + 40 + 2 = 742$
2. $80 + 7 = 87$
3. $900 + 90 + 9 = 999$

Page 79

Answers will vary. Possible answers: maid, paid, chain; day, play, say; pea, sea; plea; bee, see, free; brief, piece, field; pie, lie, tie; oat, loathe, loaves; out, round, count; food, smooth, moose

Page 80

1. $12 \div 3 = 4$
2. $20 \div 5 = 4$
3. $44 \div 11 = 4$
4. $30 \div 6 = 5$
5. $100 \div 10 = 10$

Page 81

Answers will vary.

Page 82

Answers will vary. Possible answers:
1. $12 + ? = 20$; Mr. Britton picked up 8 passengers at the second stop.
2. $11 + 6 = ?$; There were 17 passengers on the bus after the second stop.

Page 83

1. plants; fish food
2. many colors; red, gold, brown, or black
3. Answers will vary.

Page 84

Answers will vary.

Page 85

Answers will vary.

Language Arts Assessment Practice

1. In the country of Mongolia, there once lived wild horses.
2. B and D
3. Answers will vary. Sample answer: Helen Keller got sick when she was a baby. This made her become blind and deaf.
4. 3, 1, 4, 2
5. frustrated, upset; horrible, terrible; entire, whole; respect, value
6. B
7. Answers will vary. Sample answer: Brady really wanted to learn to ride his bike. He kept trying and trying. He finally tried at the park and was able to ride his bike.
8. I cant wait for school to start; Ive heard that he is the best teacher at Washington Elementary.
9. B
10. plan; ben; flite
11. A and D
12a. told
12b. sat
12c. hid
12d. said
13. Answers will vary.

Mathematics Assessment Practice

1. A, D, and E
2. 8 cups of water; Answers will vary.
3.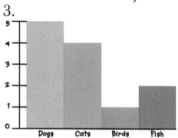
4. One more student chose dogs than chose cats.
5a. 144
5b. $100 + 40 + 4$
5c. one hundred forty-four
6a. $>$
6b. $<$
6c. $<$
7. A and C
8. B, D, and E
9. A, C, and D
10. 39
11. $1.75
12.

13a. even
13b. odd
13c. odd
14. 1; 2; 4

Kids Learn! Parent Survey

Dear Parent,

The activities in this *Kids Learn!* book have helped your child review grade-level skills from the recent school year and get ready for the year ahead. Your feedback on this learning resource is very valuable. Please complete the survey below and return it as directed by your child's teacher or school administrator. Thank you in advance for your input and your time.

Please circle the term that best describes how you feel about this *Kids Learn!* book.

1. The **Introduction** (pages 4–18) gave me good ideas for things to do with my child and offered helpful resources for extended learning.

   Strongly Agree   Agree   Disagree   Strongly Disagree

2. The **Weekly Activities for Students** (pages 20–85) were easy to understand and helped me guide my child to complete the activity sheets. The activities were at an appropriate level of difficulty for my child.

   Strongly Agree   Agree   Disagree   Strongly Disagree

3. The **Assessment Practice** (pages 86–102), which shows the types of questions that will be on standardized annual assessments, gave me and my child a better understanding of the standardized tests and how to prepare for them.

4. The sections of *Kids Learn!* that were particularly helpful or useful for me and my child were: (*Please check all that apply.*)

   ☐ Top 10 Things Your Third Grader Will Need to Know   ☐ Websites and Apps for Parents and Kids

   ☐ Things to Do at Home   ☐ Weekly Activities for Students

   ☐ Things to Do in the Community   ☐ Preparing Your Child for Assessments

   ☐ Suggested Vacation Reading and Log

Please provide any additional comments or suggestions about this *Kids Learn!* book.

_____

_____

_____

_____

Kids Learn! Encuesta para los padres

Querido padre de familia:

Las actividades en este libro *Kids Learn!* han ayudado a su hijo a repasar las destrezas de nivel de grado del reciente año escolar y a prepararse para el año siguiente. Sus comentarios sobre este recurso educativo son muy valiosos. Por favor, complete la encuesta a continuación y regrésela como lo indica el maestro o administrador escolar de su hijo. Le agradecemos de antemano por su participación y por su tiempo.

Por favor encierre con un círculo el término que mejor describe su opinión sobre este libro *Kids Learn!*

1. La **Introducción** (páginas 5–18) me dio buenas ideas de cosas que hacer con mi hijo y me ofrecieron recursos útiles para ampliar el aprendizaje.

   Totalmente de acuerdo   De acuerdo   En desacuerdo   Totalmente en desacuerdo

2. Las **Actividades semanales para los estudiantes** (páginas 20–85) eran fáciles de entender y me ayudaron a guiar a mi hijo a completar las hojas de ejercicios. Las actividades eran de un nivel de dificultad adecuado para mi hijo.

   Totalmente de acuerdo   De acuerdo   En desacuerdo   Totalmente en desacuerdo

3. La **Práctica para la evaluación** (páginas 86–102), que muestra los tipos de preguntas que vendrán en las evaluaciones anuales estandarizadas, nos dio a mí y a mi hijo un mejor entendimiento de los exámenes estandarizados y de cómo prepararse.

4. Las secciones de *Kids Learn!* que fueron particularmente útiles o nos ayudaron a mí y a mi hijo fueron: *(Por favor marque todas las que sean pertinentes)*.

   ☐ Las 10 cosas que su hijo de tercer grado debe saber

   ☐ Cosas para hacer en casa

   ☐ Cosas para hacer en la comunidad

   ☐ Registro de lectura y la lectura sugerida para las vacaciones

   ☐ Páginas web y aplicaciones para padres y niños

   ☐ Actividades semanales para estudiantes

   ☐ Preparar a su hijo para las evaluaciones

Por favor proporcione cualquier comentario o sugerencia adicional sobre este libro *Kids Learn!*

_____

#13535—Kids Learn! Getting Ready for 3rd Grade